GARRIE L. TUFFORD

DEPARTMENT OF GEOLOGY & MINERALOGY
UNIVERSITY OF MINNESOTA
MAY 17 1961

GUIDE TO THE STUDY OF ROCKS

RECENT ADDITIONS TO

HARPER'S GEOSCIENCE SERIES

Carey Croneis, Editor

Dix, *Seismic Prospecting for Oil*

Eardley, *Structural Geology of North America*

Garrels, *A Textbook of Geology*

Low, *Plane Table Mapping*

Pettijohn, *Sedimentary Rocks*

Shepard, *Submarine Geology*

Spock, *Guide to the Study of Rocks*

Praeter duritiam silicis qui talia curat

Auferat hinc aliquid; Matris et ossa colat.

A.G.C.M.

Hand specimen of dolerite, trimmed to conventional form and dimensions, natural size. Drawn by Paul Dobbs from specimen collected and prepared by Robert Daskam.

GUIDE TO THE STUDY OF ROCKS

By L. E. SPOCK

PROFESSOR OF GEOLOGY

WASHINGTON SQUARE COLLEGE OF ARTS AND SCIENCE

NEW YORK UNIVERSITY

HARPER & BROTHERS, PUBLISHERS

NEW YORK

Contents

Editor's Introduction

Sᴘᴏᴄᴋ's *Guide to the Study of Rocks* has been designed to fill a long-felt and somewhat paradoxical need for an authoritative yet relatively simple American textbook of petrology.

The paradox is found in the fact that although geology is the science of the earth not a few geologists have been inadequately trained in, or are all too little interested in, the *broad* study of the very rocks which make up the crust of that planet. Thus it is not particularly unusual to find a stratigraphic geologist who is rather lost in an igneous rock terrane. Nor is it at all rare to discover a "hard rock" specialist who is not particularly at home with the sedimentary rocks. Even some mineralogists, who are highly trained in the study of the crystallography and physical chemistry of the mineral components of rocks, may be relatively unconcerned with the rocks themselves.

Of course, the examples cited represent atypical situations growing in part out of scientific specialization; but that they can be cited at all is, on first thought, surprising because, as Dr. Spock succinctly states, "An understanding of rocks lies at the core of every geological problem." On more mature consideration, however, the surprise diminishes as one remembers that overspecialization is not the only culprit in this matter. Equally to blame has been an almost nation-wide practice of attempting to teach elementary petrology—the systematic study of rocks—through a laboratory exercise or two in a course in physical geology. Or the rocks may be considered all too briefly in the common course offering usually entitled, Rocks and Minerals. At many schools this course turns out to be no more than a sort of elementary mineralogy.

There has been, however, a growing general agreement among teachers that a relatively broad knowledge of the basic rock types is essential in the early training of all geologists. Adequate courses in the study of rocks *per se* have thus been introduced at a considerable number of institutions. These have always been somewhat handicapped, however, because of the lack of satisfactory texts, at least for the ordinary undergraduate level at which such work should first be offered. In England this situation was partly met by the publication, more than a score of years ago, of G. W. Tyrrell's *Principles of Petrology,* a text which has found considerable use in this country. But prior to the publication of Spock's *Guide* no near-counterpart of Tyrrell's *Principles* appeared in this country.

Professor Spock developed his text through considerable experimentation at New York University in a course which was open to students who had completed general geology. Commonly some of his students were enrolled concurrently in an introductory course in mineralogy. It is thus apparent from this background of pedagogical testing, as well as from the text itself, that it can be used appropriately throughout the middle undergraduate level. It also should prove to be not only a most useful general laboratory and field guide, but also a handy compendium for more mature students of the earth sciences. There is, moreover, little doubt that the *Guide* will serve widely as a reference work for those of us among the professional geologists who have unfortunately forgotten some of the rocks, or really never knew them too well as students.

The author of *Guide to the Study of Rocks,* Leslie Erskine Spock, has been unusually well prepared through training as a student, service as a teacher, and experience as a field geologist, to write the present text. He was born in London, was graduated from Cornell, and received his Master's and Doctor's degrees in geology at Columbia. After teaching experience at Cornell and Columbia, Dr. Spock joined the faculty of New York University. Subsequently he has advanced to a professorship at that institution which he has now served for well over a quarter-century. He has also had valuable experience with the American Museum of Natural History, not only in New York, but on the Museum's Central Asiatic expeditions. Through such field work Dr. Spock became more than ever impressed with the fundamental importance of the study of rocks. Now through his text, as well as in the classroom and laboratory, he will be able to project that belief to many other professional, as well as casual, students of geology.

CAREY CRONEIS

Preface

THIS volume has been prepared as a guide to the study of rocks. It is planned on the assumption that the first and most necessary step is to acquire skill in observing all the details that are visible within a rock and, through either measurement or a considered estimate, to give the various features approximate quantitative values. After a reasonable proficiency has been attained in close observation, one may proceed to the identification of rocks and begin to select and evaluate the features that are significant in interpreting their origins and subsequent histories.

In geology it is axiomatic that no environment, either at the surface of the Earth or within its outer shell, is fixed and stable, and from this it follows that no rock can be considered properly as a final product. All rocks are sensitive to change, and most of those that come within our zone of observation are undergoing transformations imposed by changing circumstances. To interpret *rigor saxorum* as a kind of *rigor mortis* is to miss the essence of geology.

With these emphases on close observation and the adjustments that tend toward equilibria, this text attempts to present the basic core of information concerning rocks that is needed by the student in the first course in petrology; one that may be extended by further study into any of the specialized divisions of Earth science. Since many students at this stage have completed general geology as their only college science course and are beginning a first course in chemistry, the earlier chapters deal principally with the physical characteristics of rocks. Concepts depending upon an understanding of elementary chemistry have been deferred with the expectation that such students will have become acquainted with chemical formulas and simple inorganic reactions by the time these are required. Similar provision has been made for those whose first course in mineralogy accompanies rather than precedes the first course in petrology. Minerals are described physically only by their appearance as grains or crystals in rocks, and only those that may be recognized by megascopic methods have been included.

Rock classification has not been stressed as a primary aim, and no one of the several established systems is followed. Although each of the systems in current use has its own merits, none has been generally accepted as a standard. Also a too formal scheme of classification tends by implication to surround each rock type with artificial boundaries that do not occur in nature, so that insistence on a rigid system obscures the necessary emphasis on gradational changes. For these reasons it seems appropriate in beginning the study of petrology to pay more attention to the recognition of rock constituents and their organization than to systems of nomenclature. Furthermore, the student will not then face the task of unlearning a particular system when he meets the refined and detailed work of more advanced studies.

No photographs of rocks have been included in the following pages. Rocks of all the common types are readily available, and it is only through continued practice in examining, testing, and describing actual specimens that the student can acquire a first-hand acquaintance. Symbols have nothing to substitute for the tactile and visual impressions that are so much a part of the familiarity and appreciation of rocks.

It is the writer's belief that in a first course in petrology, assignments dealing directly with rocks should take precedence over lists of reading matter. In accordance with this conviction, groups of suggestions appear at the ends of chapters. These are not directions for formal laboratory work, but exercises to supplement the customary laboratory training in identification and description. All have proved useful in the primary undertaking of helping the student to acquire a sense of familiarity with rocks and their content. Although some take the form of specific problems, most are cast in a more general form to indicate methods and suitable materials or to call attention to the search for significant details that are easily overlooked. A few of the procedures require the equipment and the systematic rock collections available only in the laboratory, but many are not dependent upon laboratory facilities. These can be modified according to the opportunities available in the local geology, and the

Preface

intent of the individual instructor, and then formulated as specific assignments. This practice is recommended, for both a student's appreciation of rocks and his skill grow naturally and logically from his intimate experience with actual materials.

Any textbook dealing with established subject matter is necessarily a synthesis, flavored by the prejudices of the writer as to what students ought to know. It reflects, also, the work and opinions of those whose efforts have most directly influenced the writer. It is appropriate to acknowledge especial indebtedness for inspiration as well as information to the published work of Dr. N. L. Bowen and Professors R. A. Daly and S. J. Shand, and to the teaching of Dr. C. P. Berkey and the late Professors R. J. Colony and A. C. Gill. Mr. Paul Dobbs drew the frontispiece and other figures; Mr. Humbert Revel prepared the lettered charts; Professor D. B. Chisholm and Professor Thomas N. Walthier examined parts of the manuscript. Thanks are due to all these gentlemen. The writer is grateful also to the generations of undergraduates whose various needs and responses, enthusiasms and limitations have guided this book to its present form.

L. E. Spock

Leonia, New Jersey
September 1952

GUIDE TO THE STUDY OF ROCKS

· I ·

Introduction

PETROLOGY

PETROLOGY is the systematic study of rocks; it includes the description and identification of rocks, **petrography**, and an explanation of their origins, **petrogenesis.** Further investigations seek to interpret the history of rocks by tracing the changes and adjustments that have been made in response to the changes taking place in their environment. When these studies are undertaken, petrology is extended to become a part of the other divisions of geology.

In the pursuit of knowledge, scientific studies become more and more highly specialized. Nevertheless the men and women engaged in problems of stratigraphy, structure, volcanology, mineralogy, landforms, and all the other many branches of earth science continue to call themselves geologists. Regardless of the diversity of their goals, their investigations begin with the rock framework of the earth. Hence an understanding of rocks lies at the core of every geologic problem and provides a common meeting ground for the various branches of geology.

METHOD

In the study of rocks, one skill is absolutely essential, the close, careful, painstaking observation of detail. This is a basic tool of natural science, and it is not acquired either quickly or easily. It calls for concentrated effort and continued practice until it becomes a habit, and even then no one is ever free from the danger of overlooking a significant point.

1

The time factor in geology sharply limits the use of the experimental method, consequently the vast body of geologic fact is based largely on data gathered by observation. Continued progress depends largely upon examining and understanding the implications of recorded facts.

Proficiency in observation can best be cultivated by preparing complete and systematic notes. This calls for an organized description of all the visible characteristics of a rock, so that none requires further explanation and nothing is left to memory. The accurate and orderly recording of observations is also an acquired skill and one that comes only with practice.

All rocks are aggregates, and nearly all consist of several different substances. An adequate description includes an account of the various ingredients: their color, shape, size, orientation and distribution, and it should be quantitative in so far as the amounts of these substances can be measured or estimated.

The examination of any rock begins at the place where it is collected. If the specimen is taken during mining, tunneling, or drilling operations, its location is marked and recorded as part of the normal engineering routine. A specimen collected from an outcrop must always be accompanied by a precise statement of its location and should be spotted on a map.

Rock exposures reveal data that cannot be obtained from the examination of specimens in the laboratory, and these should be recorded as far as they are pertinent to the purpose of the investigation. Some of the more obvious are structural features—the attitude of joints and lamination and the orientation of parallel lines and planes. Weathering effects should be noted, and weathered surfaces should be examined with particular care, since they often accentuate details that are obscure or even invisible in fresh material. Specimens collected for study of structure must be marked to indicate their orientation.

THE SCOPE OF PETROLOGY

The natural history of a rock is contained within the answers to these questions: of what does it consist, how was it formed, what subsequent alterations have taken place? In applying rocks to man's

2

needs the further question arises: is this rock suitable for a certain specific use? The search for the answers to these questions sets the only limits that can be placed upon petrology and prescribes the methods of investigation.

The examination of rock constituents extends petrology into the domain of mineralogy, which in turn depends upon chemistry, crystallography, and atomic structure. Here the principal tools are the polarizing microscope, the analytical laboratory, the x-ray, the spectroscope, and, more recently, thermal analysis. Petrology is concerned also with the rock substances formed by organic processes.

The investigation of the make-up of rocks cannot be divorced from the question of origin, for the various ingredients and their interrelationships betray the conditions under which rocks are formed. Many of the fundamental data of petrology have been assembled from studies of origin.

An account of all the investigations that continue to contribute to the knowledge of petrogenesis would embrace the greater part of geology. To mention a few procedures will serve to indicate their diversity. For many years, scientists at the Geophysical Laboratory and other establishments have been conducting experiments on the crystallization of minerals from solution. This work, following a definite pattern of dealing with solutions of increasing complexity, continues to throw invaluable light on the geology of igneous rocks. Other studies are concerned with the effects of high pressures. Another group is engaged in statistical analysis of the shapes and sizes of rock fragments. An entirely different statistical investigation, made possible by new techniques, is used to determine the orientation of mineral grains. Each of these methods is used to approach a different goal, but they all serve to illustrate the modern search for quantitative data.

The importance of climate in the destruction of rocks by surface processes has been appreciated for many years. Today the entire subject is being reexamined to take account of the influence of land slope as an added significant factor. In similar fashion the paleontologists and stratigraphers are directing their attention to the ecology of contemporaneous as well as ancient deposits.

In every field of human inquiry, the origin of any phenomenon is a question of the first magnitude, for origins, more than any other factor, determine whether a given philosophic system shall prevail or be discarded.

It is in no way surprising that the problem of petrogenesis have appealed particularly to men of rich imagination. Neither does it seem strange that these same problems have produced many controversies. Scientific geology was born in the midst of a conflict over the origin of basalt; it continues today accompanied by a milder debate on granite and granitization.

Any rock is the product of a definite environment in which the principal factors are temperature, pressure, and the amounts and varieties of chemical substances that are present. It is formed in accordance with the rigid laws of physical chemistry. It can be regarded as a fixed and stable unit only as long as the environment remains static. Any alterations in the conditions by which it is contained are followed by changes within the rock, adjustments that tend to bring it to a state of equilibrium with its new surroundings. A simple illustration is provided by potash feldspar. It may crystallize at a high temperature and under high pressure as part of a deep-seated intrusion. Exposed to the weather in a moist climate, it is converted to clay. This substance is readily reorganized to form micaceous minerals under the influence of relatively mild directed pressure.

The actual interpretation of rock changes is far more complex than the illustration given might imply. Many minerals are stable under a wide range of conditions and hence may have little to reveal concerning their origin or later history. Also, for the most part, the changes proceed so slowly that it is a question as to whether a rock ever attains a condition of complete equilibrium with its surroundings. It is important always to remember that any mineral is formed in obedience to the laws of physics and chemistry. It may be formed in any geological setting where suitable conditions prevail. To use a given mineral or an association of minerals as a criterion for a certain geologic process is justifiable only when the process is thoroughly understood.

A large part of petrology has to do with the alteration and reconstitution of rocks. An understanding of these changes is paramount in studies of weathering and soil formation, in the compaction and other diagenesis of sediments, in metamorphism of every kind, and the late stages of magmatic history. The first step is to determine the specific changes that proceed in response to given sets of geologic and geographic conditions. When these have been firmly established, they serve as criteria for the recognition of processes.

No rock exists in a state of isolation, each is a definite unit in the local pattern. Petrology seeks to determine the nature of contacts and the mutual influences that may prevail between adjacent bodies. An account of the relationships between rocks, added to that of their individual origins and changes, provides a record of the physical history of the region. In this way, one of the chief ends of geology is served.

SUGGESTIONS FOR STUDY

Familiarity with rocks comes only from continued practice in handling, examining, and describing specimens. This is the absolute requirement in the study of petrology. It should begin immediately and continue throughout the course. Every student should start to collect rocks as soon as possible, so that ultimately he may assemble a complete suite of specimens from the rocks locally available. The preparation of hand specimens, conventionally trimmed and systematically labeled, will greatly enrich this experience. Work done at an outcrop with a hammer teaches many lessons that precept, reading, and indoor laboratory study cannot impart. (See Frontispiece and Appendix A.)

.2.

The Examination of Rocks: Identification of Minerals

IN EXAMINING a rock specimen it is necessary to observe all the significant characteristics that are visible and to record them in a manner that will convey a clear picture of the rock to others. These requirements can best be secured through the discipline of systematic procedure in examining and describing rocks. An orderly plan calls attention to inconspicuous features that may be overlooked unless they are specifically sought: faint traces of parallel alignment, the relative freshness of minerals, whether shells are broken or intact. Organized notes avoid the common pitfall of failing to record items because they are "too obvious," or because they seem inconsequential when the examination is made. Rocks are too diverse to lend themselves to uniform treatment, hence it must not be assumed that a single, rigid schedule is to be followed or that there is merit in pursuing a certain fixed order. System is essential, not as an end in itself, but as a means of attaining thoroughness and clarity. The details of procedure should be arranged to suit the purpose and the methods of the study.

The complete account of a rock presumes that all its constituents can be identified. This goal is seldom attained by megascopic methods. The principal limiting factor is the size of the component particles. Viewed through a lens,* against a contrasting background,

* See the note on equipment at the end of this chapter.

6

grains 0.05 millimeter in diameter can be seen. The shapes of isolated minerals are visible if the dimensions are not less than 0.2 millimeter. No approximate limits can be set for the size that permits identification; this is determined by the experience of the observer as well as by the characteristics of the individual minerals.

The shapes and sizes of grains are more easily determined in a loose sand than in a massive crystalline rock. On the other hand some minerals are easier to identify on the freshly broken surface of a compact, indurated specimen. Friable rocks may be crushed to separate the grains. The operation calls for pounding with a hammer, rather than grinding in a mortar. Experience soon demonstrates which rocks lend themselves profitably to this treatment, which can be applied to poorly cemented sediments and rocks weakened by weathering, but cannot be used successfully on rocks with intimately interlocked crystals.

THE IDENTIFICATION OF ROCK-FORMING MINERALS

The identification of minerals in rocks is rendered difficult by their small size, but it is greatly aided because the minerals that commonly occur in appreciable quantities are relatively few in number. The following account deals with the most common minerals as they appear in rocks and includes only those characteristics that are useful for their identification. The observable properties are not equally reliable; cleavage and hardness are excellent criteria and can be tested. Crystal form is even better, but is displayed infrequently. Luster is a fair clue, but color must be used with discretion. In the following descriptions, "soft" means that the substance in question can be scratched by a steel point.

Cleavage

The presence of cleavage, or its absence, is especially valuable in determining minerals embedded in compact rocks. The test for cleavage is simple, but calls for practice before it can be used with confidence. Nothing is required except good illumination. The specimen is held so that light falling on the broken surface is reflected to the eye of the observer. It is then slowly rotated. An irregular surface reflects a tiny point of light that changes position but stays bright, as

7

the specimen is turned. A cleavage face is flat and serves as a plane mirror. Only at one position is light reflected to the observer, but here the entire surface is illuminated and appears bright; a slight turn carries the reflected beam away, and the surface looks dull all over. Several grains of the same mineral should be tested, as fractures may follow directions not controlled by cleavage.

Quartz

This mineral, though less abundant than feldspar, is nevertheless widely distributed. Its recognition is always important and frequently difficult. The characteristic hexagonal outline is exhibited occasionally by the phenocrysts in fine-grained igneous rocks and rarely as a secondary growth in sandstones, but in most aggregates the crystal form has no opportunity to develop. Reliance must be placed upon its hardness, freshness, and lack of cleavage. In some igneous rocks its presence is suggested or betrayed by an association of minerals that commonly include quartz. For instance, muscovite and tourmaline seldom occur in igneous material where quartz is absent. Such associations, however, only indicate the probable existence of quartz. The evidence is circumstantial.

Quartz may be clear and colorless; often it is translucent and either gray, grayish yellow, or black. The many other colors that are possible are rarely met in common rocks. Clear transparent quartz that is partly surrounded by dark minerals often appears colored and cloudy, or it may be darkened by microscopic inclusions and bubbles. The milky quartz that is usually found in veins owes its whiteness to closely spaced cracks. Detrital fragments may be frosted by wind abrasion, or they may be coated with a thin ferruginous veneer, distributed in uneven blotches. The broken surface of quartz is either sharp and jagged or irregularly conchoidal; the luster varies from that of clear glass to an oily dullness.

Feldspar

Unlike quartz, the feldspars in rocks commonly display well-formed crystals. These may occur as laths, as flat tabular plates, or as more or less equidimensional parallelopipeds. Two good cleavages are always present. In orthoclase they meet at a right angle; in other varieties the angles are slightly oblique. The luster is glassy in some, porcelaneous in others, and earthy or dull if the feldspar has suffered alteration. The alkali feldspars (orthoclase, microcline, albite) may be colorless. Microcline is often pink or ivory, orthoclase ivory or white. Plagioclase is generally white, but in some rocks the calcic varieties run from light to dark gray. Exotic colors, such as the green of Amazon stone (microcline), are rare.

Twinning affords the most reliable clue to the identification of feldspar, but is visible only on the cleavage faces of relatively coarse crystals. The Carlsbad twin may occur in any variety, but in hand specimens it can be seen only in potash feldspar. It is recognized by the unequal brightness of opposite halves of a cleavage face, the illumination being reversed by turning the specimen. All varieties of plagioclase twin according to the albite law, but the twinning striations are usually too fine to see with a lens. They are sometimes visible on the calcic plagioclase of coarse igneous rocks. The play of colors that is usually associated with labradorite may occur in any variety of plagioclase.

Feldspars affected by weathering or hydrothermal alteration look dull and earthy; they have both the appearance and consistency of chalk.

Hardness, cleavage, and form, provide a set of criteria that simplifies the recognition of feldspars as a group, and color may reveal the potash feldspar, but it is almost never possible to identify the various members of the plagioclase series. In some igneous rocks their composition may be roughly approximated from the associated minerals. Thus rocks with abundant mica, or more than thirty per cent of quartz, may be expected to contain alkali feldspar. Similarly, pyroxene in large amounts, or olivine, normally occurs with calcic plagioclase. Mineral association is not a method of identification. At best, it means relying upon experience to make a shrewd guess.

The Micas, Chlorite, Talc

Of all the minerals widely distributed through rocks, the micas are, perhaps, the easiest to identify. Their elasticity and peculiar tinsel luster serve to distinguish them from other minerals of the same general habit. The bronzy, pseudo-metallic sheen, often seen in biotite, results from weathering.

Chlorite flakes are nonelastic and display a characteristic green color. Talc is softer than either mica or chlorite and lighter in color than the latter. Rocks with appreciable amounts of talc feel soapy to the touch.

By applying pressure with a sharp steel point, flakes can be separated from all these minerals, even when they occur as minute grains. They are best studied against a dull white background.

Amphiboles

Hornblende is by far the most common amphibole; it occurs in many igneous and metamorphic rocks and may be met as grains in detrital sediments. Tremolite and actinolite are usually products of metamorphism. Other varieties are rare. Amphiboles crystallize as bladelike, shining prisms and cleave into long narrow splinters. Their hardness varies within about the same limits as ordinary steel; hence scratch tests may produce conflicting reports. The color of hornblende grades from dark greens and dark browns to black. It is often difficult, and sometimes impossible, to distinguish it from pyroxene. In attempting to make this distinction, the best clues are its satiny luster, easier cleavage, and long narrow prisms. Black glossy tourmaline may resemble hornblende, but it lacks cleavage and is triangular in cross section. Most hornblende fragments in sands retain something of their prismatic habit but are rounded at the ends.

The ordinary variety of tremolite is white; actinolite is emerald green. In their other physical properties they are similar to hornblende.

Pyroxene

Many different varieties of pyroxene occur in igneous rocks. Augite is the most common, but it cannot be distinguished in the hand specimen from the other members of the group. Most pyroxenes resemble hornblende in color and hardness, but pyroxene crystals are shorter, the cleavage difficult, and the luster less bright. Igneous rocks that carry olivine usually contain a large percentage of pyroxene. It is seldom abundant in rocks that are rich in quartz, muscovite, or biotite. It may, however, be associated with the brown mica, phlogopite.

The dull green pyroxene of metamorphosed dolomites is usually diopside.

Olivine

Olivine is conspicuous only where it appears as phenocrysts in basaltic lava. Elsewhere it can seldom be identified with a lens, partly because most crystals are small and partly because their common alteration to serpentine makes them indistinguishable among the dark minerals with which they are associated. Fresh olivine is hard and glassy and breaks with an irregular fracture. Olivine disseminated through rocks is usually greenish brown or greenish yellow rather than the green usually seen in mineralogical specimens.

Magnetite, Ilmenite

Nearly every igneous rock contains one of these minerals. Fragmental rocks may contain both. Magnetite is easily separated from loose or crushed materials by manipulating a magnet below the paper on which the sample is spread.

Nepheline, Leucite, Analcite

Nepheline occurs only in relatively rare igneous rocks. It can almost never be positively identified in hand specimens. In some localities it alters to yellow cancrinite, a mineral that suggests the presence of nepheline. Leucite and analcite are also rare, appearing in lavas. Analcite also occurs with other zeolites in basaltic rocks. Both crystallize as white trapezohedra, but cannot be told apart without optical or chemical tests. None of these minerals is likely to occur in sediments.

Calcite, Dolomite, Siderite

These minerals, the common carbonates, are all softer than steel, often crystallize as rhombohedra, and exhibit perfect rhombohedral cleavage. Most calcite is white, much dolomite slightly pink, but either mineral may display almost any color. Siderite is brown. Usually the rhombohedral faces of dolomite and siderite are gently curved. Calcite effervesces vigorously in contact with dilute hydrochloric acid; the others effervesce only in powder form, or if treated with hot acid.

Chalcedony

Cryptocrystalline silica occurs as concretions and replacements in sedimentary rocks and as a cementing medium. It is found also in veins and other cavities, encrusting the walls, or as a filler. Many detrital rocks contain chalcedony fragments.

Chalcedony deposited in open spaces is gray or white and is translucent, with a characteristic waxy luster. This variety is often precipitated in successive layers made visible by minor differences in color, texture, or translucency. The thicker bands may reveal a faint trace of fibrous structure perpendicular to the layers.

The other common varities, flint, chert, jasper, and carnelian, are structureless. All chalcedony is hard. Carnelian is translucent, somewhat glassy, and exhibits characteristic shades of orange-red. Jasper contains microscopic inclusions of hematite or limonite and may be any color from light brown to deep red. It is dull and opaque except under strong magnification.

Opal

Opal is deposited in open cavities and as a replacement. It resembles chalcedony, but is softer, and frequently exhibits iridescence. The luster is usually vitreous. It is often colorless, but reds and white are common. Much chalcedony is formed by the crystallization of opal, hence the two minerals often occur intimately mixed.

Hematite, Limonite

These compounds occur in almost endless variety; alone, in mixtures of all proportions, and intimately mixed with other substances. They may be introduced as solutions or colloids, or they may form in place by the decomposition of iron-bearing minerals.

The crystalline forms of hematite are largely restricted to ore deposits and associations of metallic minerals. Most of the hematite in rocks is present as microscopic grains disseminated through other

12

substances, or it is deposited as a crust or cementing material. A relatively minute quantity of finely divided hematite is sufficient to color the containing rock or soil a bright red, and this is a clear indication of its presence. Hematite tends to adhere firmly but unevenly to form a concealing cover on the grains in sandstone.

Limonite is a loosely used name for all the hydrated ferric oxides of which goethite is the most abundant. It is similar to hematite in determining the color of rocks and their alteration products, but the colors are less uniform. The streak of limonite may be any shade from yellow to a deep rusty brown. Since limonite alters readily to hematite, mixtures of the two are common, and the resulting colors are mixed correspondingly.

The red or brown color of an outcrop is often restricted to its surface, sometimes to a crust less than a millimeter thick. Many desert landscapes owe their vivid reds to a thin outer zone of oxidation. Both fresh and weathered material should be examined and described.

Garnet

In sands it may be difficult to distinguish garnet from red chalcedony. Elsewhere garnet is easily recognized by its equidimensional crystals, color, hardness, and glassy luster.

Pyrite

Pyrite is easily identified by its cubic form and brassy color. Pyrrhotite, the only other common mineral with which it might be confused, is attracted by a strong magnet.

Serpentine, Epidote

Serpentine and epidote commonly occur as finely divided products of hydrothermal alteration. In this form serpentine will not usually be recognized, as it possesses no sharply marked characteristics. Its dull grayish green blends inconspicuously with other minerals.

Epidote, in small grains or even finely disseminated, may be distinguished by its colors, dull greenish yellow to pistachio green. It may occur, sparingly, as grains in sandstone.

TABLE 1. The Common Rock-Forming Minerals

Mineral	Form	Cleavage, Fracture	H	Luster on Broken Surface	Colors* Name	Number	Miscellaneous	Provenance
QUARTZ	Usually none, hexagonal forms rare	Irregular fracture	7	Glassy to oily	Colorless, also white, gray, yellow, etc.		Invariably fresh	Ubiquitous
Feldspar Group								
POTASH FELDSPAR (Orthoclase, Microcline)	Equant crystals, plates, laths	Two at or close to 90°	6	Glassy, pearly, porcelaneous	Colorless, white, yellowish gray, pale yellowish brown, moderate reddish orange	5 Y 7/2 10 RY 6/2 5 YR 6/4 10 R 6/6	Carlsbad twins chalky alteration	Igneous, metamorphic rocks, detrital grains
PLAGIOCLASE SERIES		Two, slightly oblique		Glassy, porcelaneous	Colorless, white, gray		Albite twin striations, play of colors, chalky alteration	Igneous, metamorphic rocks, less common in sands
Mica Group								
MUSCOVITE	Scales, plates, "books"	One, perfect	2–2½	Glittering	Colorless to pale green		Readily separated into elastic flakes	Salic igneous, metamorphic rocks, detrital fragments
BIOTITE					Brown to black			Igneous, metamorphic rocks,
PHLOGOPITE					Grayish brown	5 YR 3/2		Metamorphosed dolomites ultrafemic igneous rock
CHLORITE	Scales, shreds	One, easy	2–2½	Silky to dull	Light green to greenish black	5 G 2/1	Brittle, nonelastic	Slates, schists, hydrothermally altered rocks Slickensided surfaces
TALC	Flakes, scales, shreds	One, easy	1	Pearly to dull	White to pale yellowish green	10 GY 7/2	Soapy feel	Schists, hydrothermally altered rock

14

Mineral	Form	Cleavage	Hardness	Luster	Color	Color code	Properties	Occurrence
Amphibole Group								
HORNBLENDE	Long, bladelike prisms	Two, oblique	5 to 6	Satiny	Dark brown and green to black		Long crystals, splintery cleavage fragments, satiny luster	Schist, gneiss, igneous rocks, detrital grains
ACTINOLITE					Dusky yellow green to dusky yellowish green	5 GY 5/2 10 GY 3/2		Igneous rocks (from hornblende), schists
TREMOLITE				Glassy, pearly	White, etc.			Schists, contact metamorphism of limestone
Pyroxene Group								
AUGITE	Short, thick prisms	Two, difficult	5 to 6	Dull to satiny	Dark green, brown, mostly black		Cleavage imperfect near 90°	Femic igneous rocks
DIOPSIDE					Dusky yellow green, etc.	5 GY 5/2		Contact metamorphism
OLIVINE	Grains		6½ 7	Glassy	Moderate yellow green and darker	5 GY 7/4	Often altered to serpentine	Femic igneous rocks
MAGNETITE	Grains		6	Metallic	Black		Responds to magnet	Igneous, metamorphic rocks, detrital grains
ILMENITE	Grains		5, 6	Metallic	Black		Nonmagnetic	Igneous, metamorphic rocks, detrital grains
NEPHELINE	Irregular		6	Glassy to greasy	White, gray		Resembles both quartz and feldspar	
LEUCITE	Trapezohedra		6	Glassy to greasy	White, gray		As phenocrysts in lavas	Comparatively rare alkali-rich igneous rocks
ANALCITE			5-6	Glassy, dull	White, colorless			Lavas, with zeolites

TABLE 1. The Common Rock-Forming Minerals—Continued

Mineral	Form	Cleavage, Fracture	H	Luster on Broken Surface	Colors* Name	Colors* Number	Miscellaneous	Provenance
Carbonates								
CALCITE	Rhombohedra, etc.	Three, oblique (perfect rhombohedral)	3	Vitreous, pearly, dull	White, any color		Effervesces with dilute acid	Ubiquitous
DOLOMITE			3–4	Vitreous, pearly, dull	White to grayish orange pink	5 YR 7/2	Rhombohedral faces gently curved	Sedimentary rocks, veins
SIDERITE			3–4	Resinous to dull	Dusky brown brownish gray	5 YR 2/2 5 YR 4/1	Effervesces with hot acid	Sedimentary rocks, veins
Chalcedony								
CHALCEDONY				Waxy, translucent	White, light gray		Banded, fibrous	Cavity lining, veins
FLINT	Nodules			Waxy	Dusky yellowish brown	10 YR 2/2		Chalk concretions
CHERT	Irregular	Conchoidal fracture	7	Dull	White, gray			Replacing limestone, bedded
JASPER	Irregular			Dull	Dark yellowish orange moderate reddish brown	10 YR 6/6 10 R 4/6		With hematite
CARNELIAN	Irregular			Glassy	Various brownish reds			
OPAL	Irregular	Conchoidal fracture	6	Glassy to dull	Various		Opalescent	Cavity filling
HEMATITE	Scales, crusts, disseminated		6	Earthy, submetallic, metallic	Sparkling black to earthy red	10 R 3/4	Red streak	Ubiquitous
LIMONITE	Crust, disseminations		5 6	Earthy, rarely vitreous	Dark yellowish orange moderate brown	10 YR 6/6 5 YR 4/4	Yellow streak to dark brown	Ubiquitous

	Habit	Cleavage/Fracture	Hardness	Luster	Color	Color symbol	Remarks	Occurrence
GARNET	Dodecahedron, trapezohedron	Sharp jagged edges	7	Glassy	Many reds and browns			Crystalline rocks, detrital grains
PYRITE	Cubes, grains	Irregular	6	Metallic	Brassy			Ubiquitous
SERPENTINE	Massive, shreds, fibers	Irregular	3	Dull to greasy	Dark greenish gray, etc.	5 G 4/1	May consist of fibers (asbestos)	Hydrothermally altered rocks
EPIDOTE	Granular	(Good cleavage not visible in grains)	6	Glassy to dull	Grayish yellow green to grayish olive	5 GY 7/2 10 Y 4/2		Hydrothermally altered rocks, contact metamorphism
GLAUCONITE	Small nodules		2	Glossy to dull	Dark greenish gray	5 G 4/1		Marine sands
KYANITE	Blades	One, perfect	5/7	Vitreous	Blue, white, green		Hardness dependent on direction	Schists
STAUROLITE	Flat prisms		7	Dull	Dusky yellowish brown	10 YR 2/2	Cruciform twins	Schists
ANDALUSITE	Prisms		7	Dull	Grayish black	N 2	Almost square in cross section	Contact metamorphism of argillaceous rocks

Note: This table lists only the megascopic properties that are useful in the identification of minerals in hand specimens. It does not take account of rare deviations from their common habit. Colors are designated by the names and numbers of the National Research Council Rock Color Chart.
* Colors are highly variable; those designated by color chart symbols are particularly common.

17

Glauconite

Glauconite occurs almost exclusively in the "greensands" which owe their name to its presence. It forms small rounded nodules of about the same size as the associated fragments. Identification depends on its shape, deep green color, and occurrence in marine sand.

Kyanite, Staurolite, Andalusite

These minerals are to be expected only in metamorphic rocks. The distinguishing features of kyanite are its long, bladed habit, perfect cleavage, hardness, and blue or green color. Staurolite forms well-shaped flat prisms, often in cruciform twins. It is brown and hard. Both of these minerals occur in schist. Andalusite is common in argillaceous rocks that have undergone contact metamorphism. It crystallizes in stout prisms that are almost square in cross section. It is dark gray and often is covered thinly by scaly, micaceous alteration products.

Clay Minerals

The individual crystals of the clay minerals are often too small to identify, or even see, under the microscope. In hand specimens clay can be seen only in bulk. Some clay minerals are formed by weathering processes, others by hydrothermal alteration. Clay occurs as a sedimentary rock, either alone or mixed with coarser particles. It enters largely into most aggregates of weathered rock. Feldspars and other minerals may be coated or completely replaced by clay.

Uncontaminated clay is white. Mixed with organic matter, hematite, or limonite, it appears gray, red, brown, or yellow.

The presence of clay may be detected by its argillaceous odor; this test should be applied to freshly broken, slightly damp, material.

Other Minerals

Several minerals are widely distributed through rocks, but for various reasons are omitted from this account. Zircon, apatite, and sphene are not described because their crystals are usually too small to be seen in hand specimens. Gypsum and anhydrite form definite rock layers and may be identified by their bulk characteristics. They are seldom found as particles mixed with other minerals. Gypsum, however, may be present as a cement or vein mineral.

NOTES ON EQUIPMENT

1. The minimum equipment for the megascopic study of rocks includes: a lens, a millimeter scale, squared millimeter paper, a steel point, a magnet or magnetized knife blade, a hammer, and dilute acid. Notes that form part of a permanent record require the use of a color chart.
2. The magnification marked on the frame of a hand lens (×6, ×10, etc.) refers to the *areal* magnification. Microscope lenses are calibrated by their lineal magnification. Linear magnification is equal to the square root of the areal magnification, hence a lens stamped ×9 yields a linear magnification ×3. For general use, a lens should have an areal magnification of not less than ×6 or more than ×12.
3. A dentist's explorer, drawn to a sharp tapering point, is an excellent instrument for testing hardness and separating minerals.
4. The Rock Color Chart, distributed by the Geological Society of America, affords a swift and accurate means for recording color. Specimens are matched against colors designated by standardized names and numbers.

SUGGESTIONS FOR STUDY

1. Examine loose sands containing these minerals: quartz, feldspar, garnet, muscovite, biotite, hornblende, magnetite, and ilmenite. Rearrange the list in the order in which you are able to identify these minerals with confidence, as particles of progressively diminishing size. List the characteristics that are most useful for their identification as mineral grains. What additional minerals, if present, might be confused with these?
2. Examine feldspars in crystalline rocks for Carlsbad and albite twinning. Also compare sanidine and quartz phenocrysts in lavas.
3. Biotite is easily distinguished from the other dark silicates in compacted rocks by the following method. Hold the specimen over a sheet of white paper, and press against the mineral with a sharp steel point. If the mineral is biotite, characteristic flat shiny flakes will separate easily. Amphiboles and pyroxenes yield only under considerable pressure, and the resulting fragments are either splintery or formless.

19

⋄3⋄

The Examination of Rocks: Physical Characteristics

THE anatomy of a rock is never simple; in addition to mineral composition, it embraces other variable factors, such as the sizes, shapes, and arrangement of the components. Within each of the classes of rocks, the compositions, textures, and structures are interrelated, and the degree of variation that may be expected is loosely set. For the whole family of rocks there is almost no limit to the theoretical number of permutations and combinations. When categories are sharply defined, the range of variation is narrowed, certain combinations are excluded, and independent variables tend to become dependent variables. For instance, nature mixes the feldspars with quartz and mica in almost endless variety. Terms such as arkose, gneiss, and granite applied to appropriate assemblages of these minerals convey a general impression of how they were brought together and impose broad limits on their variation.

The constitution of a rock is never haphazard; every detail of its mineral composition and physical organization has a definite place in an orderly plan. Even though these details vary in legibility, the examination of a rock will normally yield sufficient data to establish a pattern. Once the general pattern is clear, the nature of the more obscure features can be closely approximated. Since all the details are closely related, each must be carefully observed, whether the purpose is to identify or to reconstruct the conditions and changes of the past.

There is no general agreement as to which physical features of rocks shall be included as *textures,* and which are to be regarded as *structures.* In structural studies, **fabric** is used to include data from both categories. Nor is the lack of uniformity significant, for it is a question of sorting terms, not one of classifying phenomena. In this book texture refers to the sizes and shapes of rock constituents, together with variations in these properties. Structure covers the distribution and grouping of minerals and also the immediate effects of their arrangement, such as foliation and bedding.

Grain Size

The size of particles is best measured and recorded in metric units. The dimensions of crystals and fragments in firmly compacted rocks

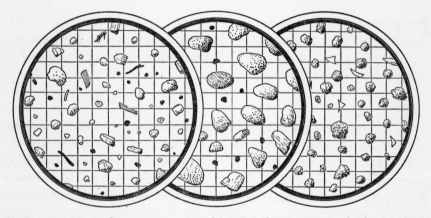

FIGURE 1. Detrital aggregates seen through a lens against a background of squared millimeter paper. **Left,** medium mixed sand; **center,** coarse sand with grains predominantly well-rounded; **right,** volcanic ejectamenta.

can be determined directly with a linear scale. This method is sufficiently accurate for grains one millimeter in diameter and larger; grains smaller than 0.5 millimeter can be described only as falling below this limit. Fragments in loose deposits and grains artificially separated by pounding can be easily and quickly measured by spreading the sample on squared millimeter paper (Figure 1 and front end leaves). By interpolation between the ruled lines, diameters may be estimated to the nearest 0.1 millimeter. Particles smaller than 0.1

21

millimeter can be seen but cannot be measured with this equipment.

Some rocks are **equigranular;** all the grains or crystals are of approximately the same size. Far more commonly they are **inequigranular.** Under these circumstances the data should include the sizes of the largest and smallest particles, together with an estimate of the size range into which the largest number falls. Most rocks are mixed aggregates, and the procedure should be applied to each set of minerals or rock fragments. This system is particularly valuable in the description of conglomerates, porphyries, and other rocks that are highly inequigranular.

Actual measurements are better than terms such as "coarse sand" and "fine gravel," even when these are used according to a rigidly fixed quantitative system. Several such systems are in use, but they apply only to sedimentary material. Many of the terms, furthermore, connote properties other than size. "Pebble," as an example, implies shape as well as a set of limiting dimensions. Such terms are an expressive part of our common speech; they should be retained in their original qualitative sense.

Shape

In dealing with the shapes of rock constituents it is convenient to distinguish between the fragments resulting from the destruction of some earlier rock body and the minerals produced by crystallization more or less in place. The distinction is usually simple and calls attention to contrasted modes of origin. Also most of the descriptive terms in current use bear a genetic connotation. Thus a feldspar phenocryst, bounded by crystal faces, is a **euhedral crystal** in its parent porphyry but an **angular fragment** when carried or deposited by water.

Of the several sets of terms applied to the shapes of minerals in igneous rocks, the most commonly used and easily remembered are those of Iddings. *Euhedral* minerals are bounded by crystal faces, **anhedral** crystals display no faces at all, and those that exhibit at least one face are **subhedral.** The definitions and subsequent usage have restricted these terms to minerals in igneous rocks. In metamorphic rocks, owing their texture to recrystallization (Becke), **idioblastic** refers to a well formed crystal, **xenoblastic** to a formless one. For the crystalline products of replacement, vein deposits, and aqueous precipitates in general, there are no widely accepted standard terms.

Equidimensional minerals have three approximately equal diameters; others are **inequidimensional.** Most inequidimensional crystals of fairly definite shape can be described as *tabular, platy, prismatic* or *acicular* (Figure 2). These terms apply also to mineral grains in detrital rocks.

The shapes of rock and mineral fragments accumulated by weathering processes or deposition are described to indicate the degree of

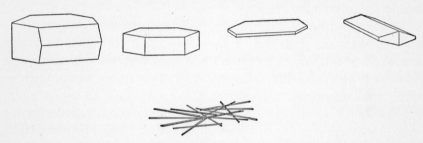

FIGURE 2.   Crystal shapes. **Upper left,** tabular; **upper right,** prismatic. **Lower,** acicular.

rounding by abrasion or solution. A *sharply angular* fragment has retained its original edges and corners. If these are blunted, but the surfaces are unmodified, the grain is *subangular.* The smoothly curved surfaces of *rounded* grains suggest neither edges nor planes.

The degree of rounding is readily observed in any clastic rock with grains that approach or exceed one millimeter in diameter. Smaller particles require separation (Figure 1). As a general rule, coarse fragments are better rounded than finer ones that have been subjected to the same transport, and those less than 0.1 millimeter in diameter are nearly all angular. Some mineral fragments retain either the form or proportions of their original habit, or of shapes controlled by cleavage. Thus hornblende is often present in sand as a long, narrow fragment with rounded ends; muscovite always appears as flakes.

Spherical bodies are formed by various processes of accretion and crystallization and may be identified either by their composition or that of the enclosing matrix. **Oolites** are typical of limestone. Closely packed oolites are generally uniform in size and may constitute the

23

entire bulk of the rock. Their easy replacement yields silicious and hematite oolites in which the spherical form is preserved.

Spherulites are common in glassy lavas, particularly obsidian. Each one consists of a globular mass of minute, fibrous crystals radiating from the center. They may be distributed at random or concentrated along definite planes.

Bauxite and residual limonite are frequently characterized by **pisolites.** Such deposites (laterites) represent a late stage in long-continued chemical weathering. Pisolites in the former consist of hydrated aluminum oxides; in the latter they are either limonite or goethite. Usually they are less than one centimeter in diameter and occur in varying sizes.

Lapilli, glassy pellets of hardened lava, are restricted to accumulations of volcanic debris.

Aphanitic Aggregates

Few aggregates that consist of fine particles are completely homogeneous and devoid of observable structural features. A careful examination of their bulk properties will usually yield sufficient information for an approximate identification. The following characteristics should be observed and recorded: color, density, hardness (resistance to scratching), fracture, texture of surface, reaction to acid, porosity, and alteration effects.

The color of an aggregate may be significant—it is never inconsequential—and should be matched against a color chart and recorded. Hematite and limonite can be identified by color, whether they appear as surface stains or are disseminated through the rock. Highly carbonaceous rocks may give a black streak; this test is aided by reducing a chip to powder.

Hardness and density are more useful in limiting the number of possibilities than for making positive identifications.

Smooth parallel fractures betray slaty foliation; a tendency to break less evenly is often an indication of fissility of bedding. An irregular and difficult fracture suggests a homogeneous rock with interlocked crystals.

Only rocks that are made up entirely of very fine particles are smooth to the touch. A few scattered crystals or grains with diameters of 0.05 millimeter or less impart a gritty feel to the surface.

Physical Characteristics

Calcareous substances and dolomite respond to dilute acid.

A drop of water will quickly spread and disappear, leaving a wet stain, when it is placed on a highly porous rock.

Some rocks consist wholly of aphanitic particles. The most common of these are listed in Table 2, with their normal, "average," properties. More often the aphanitic material represents a fraction, either large or small, of the entire rock. Examples are: the matrix of a porphyry, volcanic ash in agglomerate, clay bonding in sandstone. Iden-

TABLE 2.   Aphanitic* Aggregates

Name	"Average" Characteristics
Clay	Soft, smooth, argillaceous odor, softens in water
Clay shale	Soft, smooth, fissile
Sandy shale	Soft, gritty, fissile
Fine sandstone	Gritty, separated grains visible under lens
Graywacke	Rough, hard, difficult fracture, usually dark
Limestone	Effervesces with acid, soft, scratch yields white powder
Dolomite	Effervesces in powder, usually gritty
Ash and tuff	Gritty, soft, crumbles under hammer, usually porous
Salic lava	Rough surface, flow structure usually visible on weathered surface
Basalt	Hard, difficult and irregular fracture, high density, dark
Slate	Smooth, even, parallel, fracture
Hornfels	Smooth, hard, even fracture in one direction
Gypsum	Softer than finger nail, soapy feel, white or gray
Anhydrite	Resembles compact or chalky limestone, but does not effervesce

* *Aphanitic* was coined to describe igneous rocks with megascopically invisible particles. In the absence of a corresponding adjective to use for rocks of other or undetermined origins, the term is extended in this book to include all rocks that are similarly fine grained.

tification of the megascopic components may not establish the precise make-up of the finer part, but it will indicate the narrow range of substances that are to be expected in a normal association. Many structural features (vesicular cavities, fossils, foliation, etc.) suggest a certain mode of origin and thus similarly limit the list of possibilities.

Grouping and Orientation

The arrangement of minerals within a rock is either a **primary** structure, representing a distribution established when the rock was formed, or a **secondary** one, resulting from later reorganization.

Patches of dark minerals (biotite, hornblende) closely packed together are common in many granites. These segregations may be formless; they are called **schlieren** when they are drawn out as curving bands or wisps. Adjacent schlieren are roughly parallel.

A few igneous rocks contain **orbicules.** These are close spherical concentrations of amphibole arranged radially or of biotite in concentric-tangential pattern.

All other arrangements depend upon parallel distribution. This can be a parallel orientation of prismatic or platy minerals or segregations of like minerals within definite bands or layers. It may also be a combination of both.

Narrow prismatic crystals are sometimes ordered with their long axes uniformly parallel, after the pattern of tree trunks in a pine forest. Otherwise they follow a subparallel arrangement resembling logs floating downstream. Hornblende may show the former pattern in gneiss; the latter is encountered in the narrow feldspars of lava. Minerals of tabular or flaky habit may be similarly distributed through rocks of various origins.

Micaceous minerals drift in subparallel alignment in igneous or aqueous currents, and they come to rest with their flat sides down as they settle in air or water. In foliated metamorphic rocks, parallelism is forced upon them either by rotation or recrystallization under pressure.

Banded or layered structures arise from the segregation of minerals of like habit. In sedimentary rocks the arrangement is stratigraphic, and the differences of color, texture, or composition reflect changes in the conditions of deposition.

Many metamorphic rocks are strongly banded. The characteristic structure is one in which streaks of equidimensional crystals alternate with others consisting of flat or prismatic minerals. More often than not, the latter are oriented parallel to the banding.

True banding is rare in igneous rocks, but most lavas and many intrusives show an obscure, elusive "grain." This can be attributed to the orientation of minerals in phaneric and aphanitic rocks. In glasses it is caused by the concentration of invisible embryonic crystals into planes.

In former years, little attention was paid to the parallel organization of minerals other than for its direct relation to schistosity and foliation. More recently, rocks are being minutely examined for alignments of every sort, and the observations are yielding a vast amount of data on petrogenesis and deformation. The pioneers in these new techniques and their application are Professor Hans Cloos* and Professor Bruno Sander. Under their leadership a new branch of geology has arisen, *structural petrology*. A great part of these data must be assembled with special laboratory equipment, but much information comes directly from the examination of outcrops. Since the evidence of parallel arrangement is often faint, its detection calls for close observation. It is necessary to inspect surfaces facing in as many directions as are available; on some parallel arrangement may not show at all, on others it may fail to give a true direction, or it may be visible only on a weathered surface.

Relative Abundance

The account of any mixture, visibly heterogenous, is incomplete if it fails to include the amounts of the various components. In so far as it may be practicable, the relative abundance should be stated numerically. Equipment adapted to the microscope provides a means of making mechanical analyses by measuring and counting minerals. This method is accurate within a small margin of error that can be determined.

Estimates based upon megascopic inspection are not a substitute for precise measurement, but they are much more satisfactory than vague terms such as "predominant, widely dispersed, sparingly present." Also their accuracy is of about the same order as that of other data, assembled in the same way, and subject to the limitations that are imposed on the study of hand specimens.

Skill in approximating the amounts of minerals within a rock comes from experience born of practice. The only materials needed are specimens containing known proportions to use as a standard. The first step consists of making a "calculated guess" as to the percentage of each visible component and comparing these figures with the actual composition. When this has been sufficiently repeated, the individual learns to temper his tendency to overestimate, or underestimate, and to make due allowance for the conspicuous minerals

* Deceased, September 27, 1951.

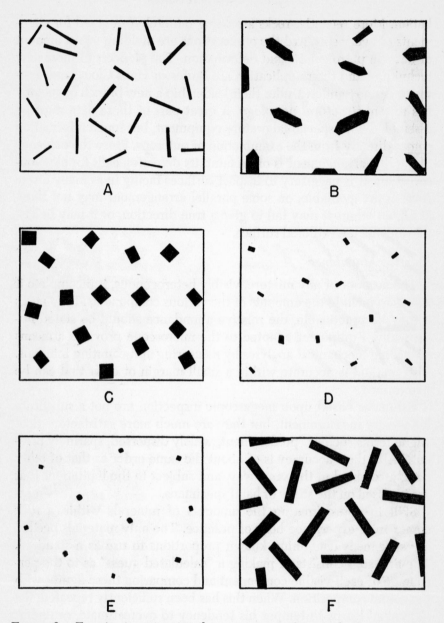

FIGURE 3. Exercise in estimating the percentages of minerals in a two-component rock. The area occupied by the black symbols in each rectangle is given in the key at the end of the chapter.

28

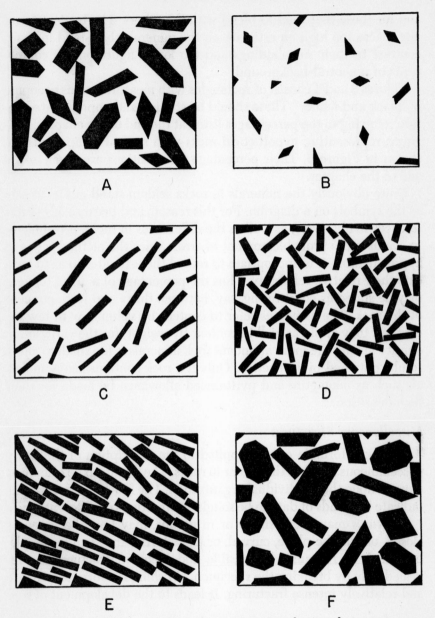

FIGURE 4.   Exercise in estimating the percentages of minerals in a two-component rock. The area occupied by the black symbols in each rectangle is given in the key at the end of the chapter.

29

and for those that tend to blend with the others. The beginner usually places too high an estimate on the minerals that stand in sharp contrast to their surroundings and too low a figure on the components of a neutral background.

Figures 3 and 4 consist of rectangles with measured areas occupied by black and white.* These should be studied and approximated before referring to the percentages listed at the end of the chapter. Diagrams representing hypothetical rocks with several components are shown in Figure 5. Their percentage compositions are given at the end of the chapter.

Quite obviously the minerals in rocks seldom stand out as clearly as the symbols on a diagram. For this reason, and because of the differences in observers, as well as the differences in rocks, it is difficult to evaluate the probable amount of error. Since the method is one of approximation, it is appropriate to record the estimates so as to indicate their relative reliability. Thus the percentage of a given mineral may be stated as constituting, say, between thirty and forty per cent of the rock. The estimates refer to content by volume; with few exceptions they apply as well to content by weight, for the variation in density among the more abundant rock minerals is too small to affect results obtained by inspection. Only if a rock contains heavy minerals such as magnetite and pyrite need allowance be made for their high densities.

Miscellaneous Structures

No single formula can be applied to the description of the many miscellaneous features that occur in rocks. The details to be examined depend upon their individual organization. The following paragraphs indicate the kinds of data to be sought in structures of different types.

Fractures may occur singly or in groups, may be either open or closed, or may be plane, curved, or jagged. Also they can be simple, branched, or reticulated. Invisible and incipient fractures are revealed only by breaking the specimen. *Crushing* is a form of intimate and relatively intense fracturing. It leads to the development of sep-

---

* A device, similar to this, but applied to the minerals in thin sections, was used by the late Professor R. J. Colony. The writer has never encountered it elsewhere or seen it published.

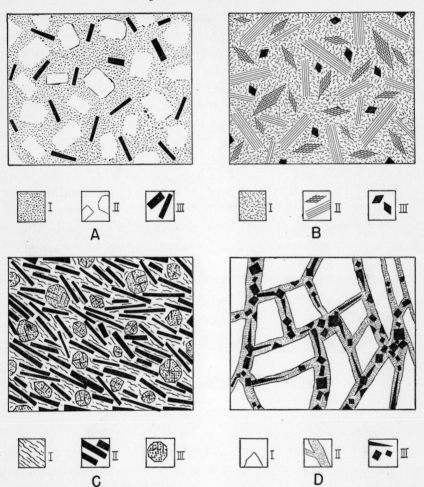

FIGURE 5. Exercise in estimating the percentage of visible components in a rock. The relative areas occupied by the symbols are listed at the end of the chapter.

arate angular fragments set in mosaic patterns. Coarse-grained rocks may be completely granulated, or remnants of stout crystals are left surrounded by a shattered matrix. If active movement accompanies the crushing, a milling action ensues that may reduce the rock to powder. Unreduced fragments are usually sharp edged and lenticular.

31

Fractures provide avenues for the circulation of fluids; hence some are enlarged by solution and others are loci for the deposition of minerals. The material that lines or closes a fracture may represent substances from the wall rock, or it may be introduced by moving solutions. A fracture filled by minerals is a *vein*.

Veins follow the patterns of fractures (Figure 6). In addition,

FIGURE 6. **Upper,** scoriaceous lava with vesicles stretched and flattened during flow. **Lower,** water-worn cobble. The intersecting fractures are filled with vein quartz. Both specimens approximately 10 cm long. Descriptions of these and other structures should include dimensions. Drawn by Paul Dobbs.

their widths are to be recorded and their minerals described. Banding, parallel to the walls, indicates separate stages of deposition.

The gas bubbles, **vesicles,** of lavas are rarely disordered. Their sizes and spacing often change systematically. The orientation of flattened and elongated bubbles indicates the direction of lava movement through the parallel alignment of their long and intermediate axes (Figure 6). Like other cavities they may be lined with minerals. Vesicles filled with minerals are called **amygdules.**

Solution cavities are common only in limestone; their walls are channeled with shallow furrows.

When fossils are present, their specific identification may or may not fall within the scope of the work. In the latter event it should at least be noted whether they are shells, bones, or leaves, etc.; whether they are intact or broken; whether scattered or concentrated along definite planes. The mode of preservation (original material, molds, casts, replacements, impressions) should be included in the description. If they are replacements, the material should be identified and described. Also it is useful to observe whether they may be easily separated or are tightly bound to the enclosing rock.

Concretions are described by their shapes, sizes, colors, and compositions. They must be broken to examine the inside for inclusions of the country rock and to reveal a possible nucleus. In the field one can observe their distribution and relationships to the bedding.

Surface Features

Nearly every natural exposure bears evidence of weathering. On some rocks this is an outer crust, on others a zone that penetrates the interior. Either one may be sharply defined or merge imperceptibly with the fresh rock. These matters are to be observed, together with their thickness, color, texture, and composition. Several surfaces should be examined to see if the weathering is related to structural features within the rock.

Grooved and polished surfaces may result from glacial abrasion, or from faulting (*slickensides*). The direction of scratches, their length, and depth are to be noted, and the polished surface should be examined for a film of secondary mineral matter. The polish that accompanies rounding is generally the result of abrasion by wind or water.

TABLE 3.   Outline for Rock Description

Specimen Number:	Location:

General Characteristics
    Texture: Color:
    Structure: Density:

Visible Components (Crystals, mineral and rock fragments)

	Name	Sizes	Shapes	%	Other Features Color, etc.
1					
2					
3					
4					
5					

Arrangement and Orientation of Minerals, etc.:

Description of Aphanitic Fraction:

Weathering, Other Alteration, Surface Features:

Additional Structures:

Evidence of Origin:

Tentative Classification:

Physical Characteristics

Ripple marks call for measurement of their length and amplitude and for a record of their symmetry and direction. *Mud cracks* are described by their pattern, depth, and curvature.

Pitted surfaces result from a variety of causes: solution, abrasion, and selective weathering that leads to the loosening or destruction of fragments and minerals. They are best described in terms of the process that made them.

Notes

At the beginning of any rock study it is necessary to prepare a definite plan for recording the essential data. The organization of a schedule will depend upon the purpose of the investigation and must be adapted to the methods that are used. There is no single scheme broad enough to include all the pertinent data in every study of rocks, nor flexible enough to fit every technique. Table 3 makes provision for the features enumerated thus far. It is not intended as an outline to be followed for the examination and description of every rock, or of any rock, but as a graphic presentation of the different kinds of significant information.

It is to be emphasized that petrology does not consist of filling in the blanks of an outline, however convenient and appropriate that outline may be. Nor is the systematic study of a rock completed by examining and recording every visible detail, even though the task has been accomplished thoroughly and accurately. Unless the observations lead to an explanation of interrelationships within the rock and an understanding of the rock as an organized whole, the procedure is monotonous and the results are sterile. Even the simplest rock calls for a measure of interpretation, in which success depends upon finding, recognizing, and evaluating the diagnostic clues. Skill in interpretation can be cultivated by experience, but it depends primarily on close observation and careful analysis. If imagination is added to these, the work is marked by style.

KEY TO FIGURES 3, 4, AND 5

Figure 3	*Figure 4*	*Figure 5*	
A 5 per cent	A 40 per cent	A I 70 per cent	C I 55 per cent
B 10 per cent	B 5 per cent	II 25 per cent	II 30 per cent

C 10 per cent	C 20 per cent	III 5 per cent	III 15 per cent
D 1 per cent	D 40 per cent	B I 68 per cent	D I 60 per cent
E 0.5 per cent	E 50 per cent	II 30 per cent	II 30 per cent
F 20 per cent	F 50 per cent	III 2 per cent	III 10 per cent

SUGGESTIONS FOR STUDY

1. Specimens similar to the one illustrated in the lower drawing of Figure 6 afford good practice in describing rocks. The example shown represents a fresh, unweathered fragment of aphanitic rock, traversed by fractures that were subsequently filled with vein material. The description of such specimens calls for completeness as well as accuracy of detail. The following features can be observed and recorded in this example, even before the student is ready to identify the rock or the vein matter.

BULK PROPERTIES:
1. Dimensions
2. Shape (rounding, sphericity)
3. Approximate density
4. Surface quality (polish, smoothness, pits, etc.)

MATRIX:
5. Texture
6. Color
7. Hardness
8. Porosity

VEIN MATERIAL:
9. Texture
10. Color
11. Hardness
12. Extent of fracture filling

VEINS:
13. Pattern (branching, reticulated, parallel, continuous, blind, etc.)
14. Dimensions (width, spacing)
15. Paragenesis (whether apparently contemporaneous, or with later veins transecting earlier)
16. Resistance to abrasion (vein material exposed as ridges or furrows)
17. Approximate amount of introduced matter

The same specimen is useful to emphasize the necessary distinction between description and interpretation. Thus the geologic history that can be inferred from the specimen includes the following events, in the order indicated:

Physical Characteristics

1. The organization into a firm rock of the material that constitutes the bulk of the specimen
2. Fracturing
3. Introduction of vein material
4. Mechanical disruption of the parent rock
5. Transport and abrasion of the fragment

2. In estimating the abundance (per cent) of constituents it is well to begin with coarsely crystalline rocks with two sharply contrasting minerals. Gradually the practice can be extended to include rocks of finer texture, more diverse content, and less conspicuous differences.

3. Several rock types are particularly suitable for beginning exercises in mineral identification, for the measurement and shape determination of minerals and fragments, and for estimates of the percentages of their components. Especially useful are porphyries with conspicuous phenocrysts, coarse arkosic sandstones, and gneisses. Banded gneiss with minerals aligned in a visible parallelism serves to introduce structure as an additional element.

ᐧ4ᐧ

Igneous Rocks

I<small>N THE</small> traditional sense of the term, *igneous* rocks are those formed by the cooling and consolidation of complex silicious solutions (*magmas*), newly risen from some deeper level. Evidence of such an origin is revealed by clean sharp contacts between the invaded and invading material, by the presence of well-defined dikes and sills, and by various details of texture and structure that can be attributed only to the movement or the crystallization of liquids. Lava flows and accumulations of volcanic fragments point even more plainly to the rise of distinct and foreign fluids. All extrusive bodies and most of those formed below the surface clearly attest to consolidation from magma. Some granites, however, and also rocks consisting of serpentine are ascribed to origins other than igneous intrusion.

One group of petrologists holds that many, if not most, granite masses have been produced by the **granitization** of deeply buried sediments and metamorphic rocks. The process calls for an invasion from below by highly mobile solutions. The original rock is so intimately penetrated by these substances and so completely reorganized that the resulting products acquire the chemical compositions and physical habits of granite. Another group ascribes a similar change to the migration of ions rather than to rising solutions. Evidence has also been cited to demonstrate that some rocks of igneous appearance and character have been formed by the local *melting* and later crystallization of nonigneous rocks at deep levels.

Igneous Rocks

The reexamination of the origin of granite* has not yet established evidence to distinguish between granite formed from magma and similar rocks resulting from granitization or local melting. Such evidence is particularly needed where the contact between granite and the adjacent rock is transitional, for in some localities granite occurs in varying degrees of physical and chemical mixture with the rock about its borders. Detailed field work combined with close laboratory study is still insufficient to fix the origin of many of these rocks. For this reason *igneous* is used here in its customary sense, for rocks formed from magmas and lavas, and to include other rocks, indistinguishable from these in hand specimens, but which may later prove to have a different history.

Texture

Texture includes the size of rock components, their crystallinity, and their shape. In igneous rocks texture is determined by the cooling history, which in turn depends upon mode of occurrence and the physical and chemical properties of the original magma or lava. A rock, consisting of grains visible to the eye or under a simple lens, is **phaneric.** This term includes so wide a range of sizes that the accurate description of a phaneric rock requires the actual measurement of crystal dimensions. The minerals in a "coarse-grained" rock might be five millimeters in diameter, or several times larger.

If the components are too small to be seen as individual particles the texture is **aphanitic.** Even though these grains cannot be measured, the relative smoothness of a fractured surface is indicative of the grain size and should be included in the description. The correspondence between fineness of texture and smoothness of surface is displayed clearly by the basalts, but it does not apply to rocks that have been altered. **Felsitic** was formerly in common use for aphanitic igneous rocks.

Most igneous rocks are completely **crystalline,** some are **glassy,** and others consist of a mixture in which glass occupies the spaces between aphanitic crystals.

* The origin of "intrusive" serpentine bodies is a problem apparently unrelated to that of granites; it is considered briefly on p. 53.

If all the minerals in a rock are of approximately the same size, the texture is **granular.** More commonly each group of minerals in a given rock falls within a fairly definite size range. When one set is conspicuously larger than the minerals that surround them, they are described as **phenocrysts.** This term refers to the relative and not to the absolute size of crystals. Phenocrysts in a glassy matrix may be just large enough to see, those in an aphanitic rock may be less than 1 mm long, whereas phenocrysts in phaneric rocks may have dimensions of several centimeters. Since phenocrysts are formed before the consolidation of the matrix, they are frequently euhedral. Rocks containing phenocrysts are described as **porphyritic.**

Apart from factors introduced by the chemical behavior of magma, a general correspondence prevails between texture and mode of occurrence, as the size and placement of the parent magma directly affects the rate of cooling. Thus most lava flows are aphanitic and many have a glassy crust and interstitial glass. Glassy rocks are all effusive.

The texture of hypabyssal intrusions (dikes, sills, laccoliths, etc.) is highly varied. Narrow dikes and thin sills are usually aphanitic. Thicker bodies often show a gradation from a finely aphanitic contact surface to a phaneric texture in the interior. Many dikes and sills are granular. Porphyritic texture is characteristic of both lava flows and small intrusions.

All the larger intrusions, batholiths, stocks, lopoliths, thick sills, and irregular masses of deep-seated origin, are phaneric. Most of them are strongly inequigranular, but phenocrysts are less common than in the smaller igneous bodies.

Pegmatites display the coarsest texture of all; they are discussed on page 107.

Minerals

Of the total number of minerals recorded from igneous rocks, only a small fraction is widely distributed, and a still smaller number constitutes the great bulk of all igneous material. The minerals that make up the greater part of a rock and, hence, determine both its gross chemical properties and its classification, are called the *essential* minerals. The list is brief:

Quartz
Potash feldspar (orthoclase and microcline)
Plagioclase
   sodic plagioclase (albite and oligoclase)
   intermediate plagioclase (andesine and labradorite)
   calcic plagioclase (bytownite and anorthite)
Pyroxene
Amphibole (mostly hornblende)
Olivine
Nepheline ⎫
       ⎬ The feldspathoids
Leucite ⎭

Accessory minerals are those which may be present without affecting the classification of the rock, although several of them are useful in interpreting the course of crystallization. No sharp distinction can be made between essential and accessory minerals. For instance, any of the minerals listed above may appear in such small quantities in a rock as to be regarded as an accessory rather than as an essential mineral. Similarly the micas occasionally are present in such large quantity that they must be considered essential ingredients. Except for the micas, most accessory minerals occur as crystals too minute to be detected megascopically. Thus apatite, zircon, and sphene are exceedingly common, but they are rarely visible. Practically every igneous rock contains a small percentage of metallic minerals, usually either magnetite or ilmenite. These also occur as small grains, but the magnetite can often be separated from a crushed sample with a magnet.

All the minerals listed thus far crystallize directly from magma or lava. In this sense they may be called **primary.** However, it frequently happens that fluids are trapped within the interstices of freshly consolidated rock. These substances are hot, mobile, and active; they represent the final fraction of the magma. Characteristically they react with the previously formed crystals to form a set of **secondary** minerals. Among these the most common are: chlorite, serpentine, epidote, various "clay" minerals, carbonates, and fine shreds of muscovite. These are products of rock alteration, but they are developed as part of the igneous history and so should not be confused with the effects of weathering.

41

Mineral Association

The broad principles that determine the combinations of minerals that may be expected in igneous rocks are explained by the laws that govern the crystallization of magma. This matter is considered in Chapter 6. There are, however, a few empirical rules that aid the identification of both minerals and the rocks that contain them.

1. Quartz does not occur in igneous rocks that include olivine, nepheline, or leucite.
2. Potash feldspar and plagioclase often appear in the same specimen, but two different kinds of plagioclase almost never occur together.
3. If the amount of potash feldspar is equal to or greater than that of plagioclase, the plagioclase is probably albite or oligoclase.
4. If muscovite is present, the plagioclase is a sodic variety.
5. In rocks with olivine, or with more than forty per cent of dark minerals, the feldspar is either labradorite or calcic plagioclase.

Classification of Igneous Rocks

In scientific studies classification serves several purposes, but the principal aim is to establish an orderly, logical plan for the arrangement of data. A classification places similar phenomena together and calls attention to the differences that separate unlike phenomena. Many systems are genetic and require an interpretation of the history of the materials; differences based upon origin precede those arising from form or content. A classification scheme also provides a group name (less often a number) for the objects in each of its categories. Hence each name implies a set of more or less limiting characteristics.

Texture and mineral composition form the bases for nearly all the many classifications of igneous rocks. Some systems take cognizance of field relations and so require one set of names for hypabyssal rocks, and another for effusive rocks, of similar texture and composition. Several classification schemes are quantitative, others partly so, and some are purely qualitative.

In earlier days confusion resulted from the continuous introduction of new names. Many names were invented to describe minor differences within common and well-known rocks. Others were given to rare combinations of minerals that may have been observed in a single isolated outcrop. Thus geology became cluttered with more names than even the specialist in igneous petrology could remember.

More recently, several excellent and practical classifications have been developed. They have reduced the number of names and provided logical arrangements that are both simple to use and easy to remember. Wisely most authors have avoided coining new names and have retained those established by custom. The general acceptance of any one of several alternative classifications in current use would do even more to simplify rock nomenclature. Unfortunately, difficulties yet remain, for in adhering to the better known rock names, each author has applied definitions in terms of the basic principles that underlie his own classification. Also they have not been unanimous in selecting and rejecting names from the earlier days of petrology. In this way two different names may stand for the same combination of minerals and texture. Also the same name, used in two different classifications, may not be employed in precisely the same sense in both.

Most igneous rocks may be considered as mixtures, closely related to other and quite similar mixtures of like origin. Names are applied to them as a matter of convenience. Several contrasted rocks may occur within a single intrusion, and yet the transition from one texture or one grouping of minerals to another may be so gradual that it is impossible to mark their separation. Even in a rigidly quantitative laboratory classification borderline rocks appear. Hence it is important to remember that the lines ruled on a formal classification chart serve only to separate the *names* applied to rocks. Actually they represent transition zones between related mixtures. In Appendix D the names of the common igneous rocks are arranged to indicate their compositions and presumed relationships.

PHANERIC ROCKS

The rocks that make up the greater part of the large intrusions and that are therefore by far the most abundant are the most easily classified. Even though their variety is considerable, they may be represented as a series ranging from granite to gabbro. Except for some that may not have been produced from magma, their history seems to follow a common plan. The evidence for this is based upon field relations and study with the microscope, and the course of crystallization is corroborated by experiment.

The phaneric rocks that cannot be included within this series almost never occur as large intrusions. With few exceptions they appear either as local facies of a larger body or as relatively small intrusions. These less common rocks are as varied as they are rare, and it is largely to them that petrology owes its great number of rock names. For many of these rocks it can be demonstrated that the departure from a "normal" mineral assemblage results either from the separation or concentration of crystals apart from the fluid magma. Others appear to result from chemical reactions between the magma and its walls or roof. Each one presents a separate problem in petrogenesis.

The Granite-Gabbro Series: Granite

Granite is a phaneric igneous rock in which the essential minerals are potash feldspar and quartz. The feldspar may be orthoclase, microcline, or both, and frequently a small quantity of sodic plagioclase is present as an accessory ingredient. Feldspar seldom constitutes less than sixty per cent of the rock. Most granite contains from twenty to thirty or thirty-five per cent of quartz. When this mineral falls below ten or fifteen per cent, the crystals are often small and tend to be concealed by the others. With less quartz the rock may be described as a **quartz syenite;** without quartz, it is called **syenite.** Megascopic crystals of biotite are present in most granites. Hornblende and muscovite are less common accessories, and granite with pyroxene is rare. Few granites are free from magnetite, but the magnetite grains and other minor accessory minerals are too small to see.

In comparison with the other common intrusives and among crystalline rocks in general, granite is a rock of low density. It owes this property to the relatively small quantity of femic minerals and to the low specific gravities of quartz and potash feldspar.

The color of granite is determined by the color of the feldspars, and the amount and distribution of the dark accessories. The quartz is usually either colorless or a neutral gray and hence serves only to dilute the prevailing color of the rock. Granites range from deep to pale red, from dark gray to almost white. A few are yellow. The texture varies from rocks with minerals several centimeters in diameter to others with barely visible crystals. Most granites are strongly inequigranular and some are porphyritic. One variety, **aplite,** is granular with an even, sugary texture and minerals less than 1 mm in diameter. Its equidimensional crystals impart a striking homogeneous appearance. It occurs as dikes cutting larger granitic intrusions.

Granite has a wide distribution through the lithosphere, occurring as batholiths, stocks, dikes, occasionally as sheets, and often as irregular masses. Also, because of the wide range of colors and textural patterns, the granites exhibit an extreme diversity of appearance. Nevertheless, no two granites from separate intrusions are ever quite the same. Specimens which at first glance appear to share similar colors and textures are readily told apart on closer inspection. Typical granite is easy to identify, but not all are typical. Granite, no less than other rocks, may pass through transitional stages into other varieties. Thus some rocks are intermediate between granite and gneiss, others occupy indeterminate positions between granite and granodiorite or syenite. For such rocks no single names are adequate; rather they call for explanations of the properties that serve to link them to the rocks that they relate.

The Granite-Gabbro Series: Gabbro

The essential minerals of gabbro are plagioclase and pyroxene, with or without olivine. The presence or absence of this mineral is indicated by the names **olivine gabbro** and **olivine-free gabbro.** The feldspar is intermediate to calcic, usually close to labradorite, and constitutes approximately half the rock. Several different varieties of pyroxene may be present, but they cannot be distinguished megascopically. If amphibole occurs, it commonly represents an altered pyroxene. Ilmenite is the usual metallic mineral.

Nearly every gabbro (together with the related dolerite and many basalts) exhibits a distinctive textural pattern. The feldspars crystallize as short, straight laths, arranged at random in a three-dimensional network. The dark minerals occupy the remaining space. In some gabbros the order is reversed, with pyroxene providing the framework and feldspar within. This intimate interlocking makes the rock difficult to break. It also explains the peculiar and characteristic mottled appearance that arises from either dark or light minerals seen as islands surrounded by contrasting crystals.

The texture of gabbro is more clearly related to the cooling history than that of other igneous rocks. Thick sheets of gabbro may be excessively coarse within, but the grain size decreases sharply close to the margin, with the rock at the contact completely aphanitic. Thus a sill or lopolith of gabbro may have a basalt border facies.

Dolerite* differs from gabbro only in texture; it is a finely phaneric assemblage of the same minerals arranged in the same pattern. Its finer texture and the difficulty of observing individual crystals give it a false appearance of being homogeneous and granular. It occurs mainly as sills and dikes and, like gabbro, tends to grade into basalt close to the cooling surfaces.

Neither gabbros nor dolerites are likely to contain phenocrysts. They are dark colored, partly because the dark minerals make up about half the rock and partly because the feldspar itself may sometimes be almost black. Similarly these rocks are heavy; they owe their high density to iron-bearing minerals, such as pyroxene and olivine, and to the specific gravity of labradorite, which exceeds that of orthoclase and sodic plagioclase.

Granite-Gabbro Series: Intermediate Rocks

Between granite at one end of the series and gabbro at the other, there is no limit to the number of intermediate stages that may be set. Divisions are necessarily arbitrary and depend upon whatever classification is employed. Furthermore the variation does not follow a single line. The mineral compositions of igneous rocks can be represented within a three-dimensional framework, but they do not lend themselves to plotting along a curve. The following tabulation is given as a basis for further description. The names are used with

* *Diabase* is frequently used as a synonym for dolerite; however, it has been employed with other meanings and for this reason is a less satisfactory term than dolerite.

46

their generally accepted meanings, but they are intended as guides and not as definitions.

> Granite
> Granodiorite
> Quartz Diorite
> Diorite
> Gabbro

Feldspar is the only mineral invariably present in these rocks, also its composition varies progressively through the series. Hence it is convenient to use feldspar as a reference for the comparison of other mineralogical changes. Potash feldspar is the predominant mineral in granite; plagioclase is either subordinate or absent. Some classifications employ the term **quartz monzonite** for rocks with potash feldspar and plagioclase in approximately equal amounts, but this name is gradually being discarded. In granodiorite, potash feldspar is a minor mineral, and in diorites and gabbros all the feldspar is plagioclase. Through the series, the plagioclase undergoes a progressive change from sodic varieties in granite to either labradorite or bytownite in gabbro. The feldspar of granodiorites and diorites is close to andesine.

The foregoing description should not be interpreted to imply that progressive changes, in this order, are to be expected in any one region, however large, where transitional stages link together a number of igneous rocks. Even less are they likely to be found within a single rock body that exhibits marked variation. The same warning applies also to the other mineralogical changes. The sequence from granite to gabbro serves only to illustrate widely represented combinations of minerals.

Quartz is abundant in most granites, sparingly present in a few, and, on the average, decreases through the series. It last appears as an essential mineral in quartz diorite. Nevertheless few diorites are free from quartz. In them it is regarded as an accessory.

At the granite end of the series biotite is by far the most common dark (visible) accessory, with hornblende next and pyroxene rare. Hornblende is characteristic of the diorites, and in older classifications it was considered an essential mineral. Either biotite or pyroxene may be present in the diorites, sometimes to the exclusion of hornblende. Gabbro requires pyroxene, and olivine gabbro calls for both pyroxene and olivine. Qualitatively the change is a progression from biotite through hornblende to pyroxene and olivine. Quantitatively there is an increase in the dark constituents. Granites may contain less than one per cent and seldom more than fifteen per cent. Gabbro and dolerite usually contain about equal amounts of feldspar and dark minerals. The mineral compositions in the granite-gabbro series are summarized in Table 4.

TABLE 4. Common Rocks of the Large Intrusions

| Rock | Essential Minerals | | Accessories |
	Feldspar	Other	
Granite	Potash feldspar	Quartz	Biotite, hornblende, sodic plagioclase (pyroxene)
Granodiorite	Intermediate plagioclase potash feldspar subordinate	Quartz	Hornblende, biotite (pyroxene)
Quartz Diorite	Intermediate plagioclase	Quartz	Hornblende, biotite, pyroxene
Diorite	Intermediate plagioclase		Quartz, hornblende, biotite, pyroxene
Gabbro	Intermediate to calcic plagioclase	Pyroxene ±olivine	Hornblende

The increase of dark constituents toward gabbro is reflected by darker colors and higher specific gravities. These changes, however, do not follow an even progression. Color and density, considered together, are useful guides to the approximate character of an igneous rock, but the actual identification of a specimen requires the recognition of all the major constituents. Some rocks can be identified precisely, others can be placed within approximate limits, but for many a description of the visible components must suffice.

Large batholiths consist predominantly of quartz-bearing rocks. Gabbro occurs as intrusive sheetlike masses; it is the characteristic rock of thick sills and lopoliths.

Syenite and Nepheline Syenite

Syenite and nepheline syenite are comparatively rare rocks, together constituting only a small fraction of all igneous matter. Nevertheless the nepheline-bearing rocks in particular have attracted the close attention of petrographers, for they embrace many different combinations of minerals. Rocks in this category from one locality seldom resemble those from another. Two widely separated granites may be superficially alike; basalts collected from five different continents may be almost identical, but each nepheline rock is distinctive. Several theories have been advanced to account for their origin, but the evidence now available does not suggest that all may have formed in the same fashion.

SYENITE resembles granite, the chief difference being that quartz is absent or else present in minor amounts as an accessory mineral. The explanation lies in the ratio of silica to the other chemical components. Silica is the one ingredient common to all the quantitatively important minerals of the igneous rocks; the feldspars, amphiboles, pyroxenes, and micas are all silicates. Orthotectic quartz represents silica in excess of the amount required for the crystallization of these minerals.

The only essential mineral of the syenites is feldspar, either sodic plagioclase or a potash feldspar. If these are present in approximately equal amounts, the rock may be called **monzonite.** The common accessories are biotite, hornblende, and soda-bearing pyroxenes. Syenite is pink or gray, taking its colors from the feldspars and modified by the dark minerals.

NEPHELINE SYENITE contains alkali feldspar and nepheline. Nepheline appears only if the silica is insufficient to complete the crystallization of albite. Hence it is never found with quartz. Nepheline frequently alters to *cancrinite,* a mineral easily recognized by its distinctive straw yellow color and waxy luster. This mineral is a reliable clue to the presence of nepheline. Without cancrinite, the identification of nepheline syenite in hand specimens is either difficult or impossible, as nepheline in grains less than 2 mm or 1.5 mm in diameter is easily confused either with quartz or feldspar. Pyroxene is more common and more abundant as an accessory than in

49

either granites or the syenites. The other visible accessories are biotite and hornblende.

The syenites and nepheline syenites may be represented as a series related to granite:

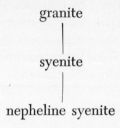

granite

syenite

nepheline syenite

The principal change in the sequence is brought about by the decrease in silica, already noted. It is marked by the disappearance of quartz followed by the substitution of nepheline for all or part of the sodic plagioclase. A parallel change is the increase in sodium and potassium, the elements that characterize the alkali feldspars. Sodium is a major constituent of nepheline and enters into many of the pyroxenes found in these rocks. Syenites and nepheline syenites occur almost exclusively in regions where the granites are rich in alkalies.

Rocks with relatively large amounts of sodium and potassium and containing nepheline or leucite, and related to gabbro are also known. However they are too rare to be included in this account.

Rocks Related to Gabbro

Several rocks of relatively simple mineralogical composition occur in close association with gabbro. Chemical studies and the field relations of these rocks indicate that they have formed from magma of gabbroic composition. Three of these rocks are essentially **mono-mineralic,** that is, they consist preponderantly of one mineral:

ANORTHOSITE: intermediate or calcic plagioclase
PYROXENITE: pyroxene
DUNITE: olivine

Any of these rocks may contain minor amounts of other minerals. A fourth group of rocks, **peridotite,** is a mixture of pyroxene and olivine. In some localities its association with gabbro is clear, but in other regions it occurs separately, with no apparent connection with other igneous rocks. Pyroxenite, dunite, and peridotite are distinct from other igneous rocks in that they alone contain neither feldspar nor minerals related to feldspar. In them the magnesium-iron content is much greater than in other igneous rocks, and they consist only of dark minerals. Hence they are loosely grouped as the **ultrafemic** rocks. Figure 7 indicates schematically the essential minerals of these rocks in relation to gabbro.

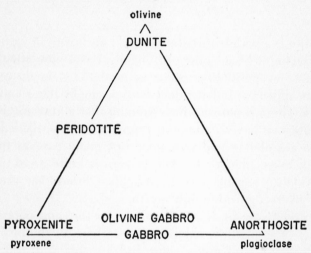

FIGURE 7. The essential minerals of gabbro, anorthosite, and the ultrafemic silicate rocks. For an explanation of three-component diagrams see Appendix C.

ANORTHOSITE is made up of a single plagioclase feldspar of either calcic or intermediate composition. Minor amounts of pyroxene may be present, and some anorthosites contain garnet. The feldspar is fresh and occurs as coarse lathlike crystals that may exceed ten millimeters in length. Many anorthosites have been crushed and consequently exhibit a pronounced **cataclastic** structure. This is manifested by a granular-mosaic appearance that affects all but the centers of the larger crystals. If these remain intact they lack sharp boundaries with the surrounding crushed material. Anorthosite is white, or gray, or the play of colors of the plagioclase may impart a bluish shade.

PYROXENITE resembles gabbro, but its texture is usually finer, with crystals not more than two or three millimeters long. Pyroxenite is darker than gabbro, and heavier. Its high density results partly from the lack of feldspar and the preponderance of femic silicates and partly from the relatively high content of metallic minerals. Pyroxenites may contain sulfides and chromite as well as the more common heavy metallics.

DUNITE is a rare rock consisting of olivine, with no other mineral in appreciable quanity. It is green, granular, and heavy.

Peridotite

Peridotite is a widely distributed rock, occurring in various forms and embracing a broad range of chemical and mineralogical compositions. Some peridotites occur as gradational facies of gabbro, but others appear as independent bodies, chiefly dikes and pipelike intrusions. There is no basis for assuming that all the rocks grouped in this category have a common origin. The essential minerals of peridotite are olivine and pyroxene, but many contain the brown magnesian mica, phlogopite. The texture is more or less granular. Most peridotite has been so thoroughly altered that the original minerals are recognizable only by their shapes. If mica is present, it may be relatively fresh, but the rocks for the most part consist of aggregates of serpentine, chlorite, and carbonate. Hence most peridotites display a dull green color and are soft and easily broken under the hammer. If alteration has proceeded so far that no suggestion remains of the shapes or cleavage surfaces of minerals or of an igneous texture, hand specimens of the rock cannot be distinguished from those of massive serpentine.

The *kimberlites* constitute a distinct group of peridotites found in pipelike intrusions. They are nearly always severely altered, and almost invariably crowded with angular fragments of wall rock. Characteristically the walls are steep and the cross sections are approximately circular. Many are brecciated. This structure and the intimate mixture of kimberlite and wall rock point to explosive activity. The rock takes its name from the famous African diamond locality.

Igneous Rocks

Serpentine

The tern serpentine is used in two senses. It is applied to a group of minerals that includes the fibrous asbestos, chrysotile, and other compounds of similar composition but less striking physical properties. It is used also for the rocks that consist preponderantly of these minerals. As a distinct rock, serpentine occurs as intrusive masses. In hand specimens it may be firm and compact or soft and fibrous. The colors range from deep green and greenish yellow to dull greenish grays. Some serpentines are red. The color may be uniform or mottled. Asbestos veins may be present. Some serpentines display slickensides that bear no apparent relationship to faults.

The origin of serpentine is obscure and constitutes a major problem in petrogenesis. Formerly, most serpentines were regarded either as direct precipitates from magma or as the products of the immediate alteration of peridotite. Chemical evidence, based on laboratory experiments, has cast serious doubt on both these modes of origin. As alternatives to a "normal" igneous origin, it has been suggested that serpentine may be injected upward as a solid mass or as a loose aggregate of crystals lubricated by interstitial fluids.

STRUCTURES IN PHANERIC ROCKS

Joints

Every igneous rock body is cut by joints arranged in more or less well-defined sets. Some joints result from the contraction that invariably accompanies cooling, others may be related to the movement of the magma before final consolidation arrested its flow. Still other joints may be produced by later stresses. Even though a study of the joint pattern may not fall within the scope of a particular petrologic investigation, the attitude and spacing of the joints should be measured and recorded at each outcrop where specimens are collected.

FLOW STRUCTURE is present in nearly every igneous rock, although in many it can be detected only by an exhaustive statistical analysis of the minerals in oriented thin sections. The flow structures in

53

phaneric rocks indicate the directions of movement within a magma at a stage when it is largely crystallized, but still sufficiently mobile to move as a viscous fluid. The megascopic evidence of flow is seen in various parallel arrangements: the linear or platy alignment of minerals, the direction of light or dark contrasting streaks, and the orientation of foreign inclusions. When such parallelism can be observed it is usually more pronounced near the margins of the rock body and close to inclusions. It tends to follow and imitate the form of the contact surfaces. Flow structure is seldom visible in the inner parts of large intrusions. The most conspicuous evidence of flow is given by the subparallel arrangement of dark minerals, usually either biotite or hornblende and, less often, by alternating bands caused by the local concentration of light or dark colored minerals. In some rocks the flow structure is either obscure or invisible on fresh specimens, but can be seen on exposures where differential weathering has etched the surface by attacking the more susceptible minerals. Unless the structure is unusually strong, the parallel elements can be observed only on planes that include their particular direction. Hence it is necessary to examine surfaces of several different orientations. It is also essential to record the orientation of flow with respect to joints.

Inclusions

Many intrusive rocks contain **xenoliths**, inclusions of foreign rock gathered from the walls or roof or torn loose at lower levels and transported upward by the rising magma. Field observations of xenoliths should include a record of their orientation with respect to other xenoliths and to the lines or planes of flow in the enclosing igneous rock and also to the contact of the intrusion. In addition it is important to compare the attitude of the structures, such as foliation and bedding within the xenoliths, to the strike and dip of related structures in the wall rock. These data indicate the direction of magma movement and show whether the xenoliths have been turned from their original positions.

Xenoliths may show no evidence of attack by the engulfing magma, other than their separation from the parent rock, or they may be strongly modified. In general, xenoliths suspended in large granite intrusions are more altered than those found in other rocks and in smaller intrusions. The effects may be purely mechanical, such as the invasion of magma along planes of weakness, or they may result from chemical reaction between xenolith and magma. Such reactions may be arrested at a stage when only the outer or the invaded portion of the xenolith has been modified, or the changes may continue until the entire xenolith has been digested and incorporated in the magma. In some intrusions xenoliths may occur in various degrees of alteration, exhibiting the successive stages of the assimilation process.

Magmas that crystallize to form the quartz-bearing intrusives react with many xenoliths to produce minerals identical with those that precipitate directly from the magma. The explanation of this process and of the limits within which it can operate is a corollary of the *reaction principle* established by Dr. N. L. Bowen of the Geophysical Laboratory. The reaction principle is summarized in Chapter 6.

A typical example would be provided by the immersion of a block of hornblende schist in a magma that is crystallizing to produce a biotite granite. Under these circumstances the magma reacts with the hornblende to produce biotite. It is to be emphasized that this is a direct chemical reaction between solid hornblende and liquid magma and that the hornblende is neither melted nor dissolved during the process. Frequently the outer shape of a xenolith may be preserved and its foliation, or other structure, may remain intact even though its chemical make-up has suffered a complete change. At a more advanced stage the minerals of the xenolith may become separated and their parallel alignment destroyed, so that the position of the xenolith is marked only by a patch of granite, darker than its surroundings because of the local concentration of biotite. If movement occurs before the final consolidation of the rock, the dark patch may be drawn out to form a dark streak indistinguishable from schlieren formed in other ways. Several of these possible modes of occurrences are shown schematically in Figure 8.

The significance of the assimilation process lies in its effect upon the magma. A magma of composition A, assimilating xenoliths of composition B, will crystallize finally as a mixed product consisting of both. Many rocks with rare or peculiar compositions have been explained as the result of such assimilation.

In sharp contrast to the effects just described, many intrusions contain xenoliths that show no tendency toward assimilation. Their failure to react with inclusions may have been caused either by a too rapid rate of cooling or to chemical inertia between magma and xenoliths.

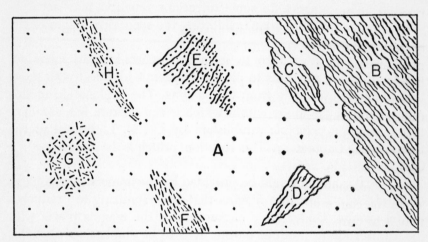

FIGURE 8. Xenoliths in granite. **A,** granite. **B,** schistose wall rock. **C,** slab detached from wall, foliation retains original orientation. **D,** xenolith tilted, but otherwise unaltered. **E,** xenolith invaded by magma along planes of schistosity. **F,** xenolith largely converted to new minerals, but retaining shape and suggestion of schistosity. **G,** patch of dark minerals marking position of xenolith now destroyed. **H,** dark minerals drawn into streak by movement of magma.

GLASSES

Glassy texture results from rapid cooling; hence rocks consisting wholly or predominantly of glass occur either as lava flows or as accumulations of volcanic fragments. Many lavas of stony appearance contain appreciable quantities of glass concealed as a residue between the crystals. An outer zone of glassy texture may also appear at the surface or contacts of lavas and small intrusions where the drop in temperature has been sufficiently rapid.

Any lava will harden to glass if suddenly chilled, and glasses of many different compositions have been described. However the rate of crystallization depends upon the viscosity as well as upon the rate of cooling. Lavas that remain relatively fluid at low temperatures tend to produce crystals; the most common glassy rocks are formed by the cooling of the more viscous lavas. For this reason most glasses have a composition close to rhyolite, whereas basaltic lavas are usually crystalline. Basalt is far more common than all other types together, but basaltic glass (tachylyte) is comparatively rare except as a chilled border phase.

In contrast to the orderly geometrical packing that characterizes crystalline structure, the ultimate chemical constituents (ions) of glass are arranged at random. Hence glass is to be regarded as a highly viscous solution rather than as a true solid, even though it is markedly hard and brittle. Because of the haphazard spacing of their components, all glasses have lower densities than their crystalline equivalents. The composition of a glass can be determined only by chemical analysis. For this reason glasses are named and described in terms of their conspicuous features. As an example, any glassy rock containing phenocrysts may be called a **vitrophyre**; only when the composition of the rock has been established as a rhyolite may it be termed a rhyolitic vitrophyre.

Texture, Structure

Theoretically a lava might cool to form a completely homogeneous glass, free from crystalline material and devoid of structure. In nature this condition is never realized and seldom approached. Most glasses are crowded with embryonic crystals (**crystallites**), so small that they are visible only under high magnification. The crystallites are usually concentrated along wavy bands by the moving lava and so constitute a primary flow structure. In some rocks this is reflected by streaks of contrasting color or color density; in others it is faintly suggested by almost imperceptible lines. Flow is visible in the hand specimens of most glasses, but it is seldom strong enough to disrupt the characteristic conchoidal fracture.

Phenocrysts, when present, are nearly always euhedral.

Vesicular cavities are formed when bubbles of escaping gas are arrested by the increasing viscosity of the cooling lava. In **pumice** they constitute the greater volume of the rock. Their shapes and sizes vary. If the lava was at rest, the vesicles tend to be spherical, otherwise they are drawn into flat ovals or tapering tubes parallel to the direction of flow. Their size and concentration diminish toward the surfaces where the greater viscosity of the cooler lava has retarded the formation of bubbles and inhibited their tendency to coalesce.

Gas cavities lined with mineral matter are called **lithophysae** ("stone bubbles"). The fine stony substance may be produced by the hot, imprisoned gases attacking and altering the adjacent glass, or it may consist of crystals (often tridymite) precipitated by the gas. Vesicular cavities filled with minerals are known as **amygdules.** Unlike lithophysae the minerals of amygdules (calcite, chalcedony, zeolites) are usually introduced by solutions from without.

During the cooling of glass, contraction stresses are set up that occasionally result in **perlitic** structure. This consists of large numbers of small curved fractures arranged tangentially about centers of cooling. When the structure is strongly developed, the rock may be separated into small (1 to 4 mm) spherical pellets, **perlites.**

Spherulites are globular aggregates of fibrous or finely acicular crystals, radiating outward from a common center. They consist of quartz, feldspar, or both. Their origin cannot be determined from the hand specimen; some are formed by rapid crystallization about a nucleus in fluid lava; others may be formed by crystallization from rigid glass. Often they are aligned along the planes of flow.

Devitrification

Glass is an unstable substance. Because its components are spaced without plan, at unequal distances, the forces of attraction that surround a "particle" are unbalanced. Ultimately the components succumb to the unequal stresses and are drawn together to form crystals. This process, crystallization from a glassy phase, is known as **devitrification.** Sooner or later it affects every glassy rock; no geologically ancient glasses have ever been recorded. Crystals formed by devitrification are excessively small; so that devitrified rocks are correspondingly fine grained. Completion of the process turns a glass into a dense, stony paste, but the earlier stages may be selective and begin with the crystallization of only one component. Devitrification is frequently controlled and guided by the flow pattern and produces a strongly banded appearance.

Obsidian

Obsidian is a term applied to glasses with shiny luster, dark color, and smoothly conchoidal fracture. Most obsidians are rhyolites, but they are not limited to this composition. Typical fresh obsidian is glossy and black, owing its darkness to closely spaced crystallites. Light passes readily through thin flakes and tapering edges. Although most obsidian appears homogenous at first sight, close inspection will usually reveal traces of flow lines. Spherulites and lithophysae are common structures, and phenocrysts of quartz or feldspar are present in many.

Hematite, dispersed through the rock as a finely divided powder, may give obsidian a deep red color. It marks an early stage of devitrification. The red color is usually not persistent, but is distributed in patches or concentrated in streaks that follow the lines of flow.

In many localities of recent volcanic activity rhyolitic glass is light gray in color and strongly banded. The color and pronounced flow layers preclude its description as obsidian, but nevertheless it is a phase of the same material. The light color may result from partial devitrification or from the stretching of small vesicular cavities along the flow direction. There is no term in general use for this rock; most of it represents an intermediate stage between massive obsidian and typical pumice.

PITCHSTONES are glassy rhyolites with a resinous rathen than a glassy luster. Their appearance is ascribed to an abnormally high water content. Typical colors are green, brown, and gray; otherwise they resemble obsidian.

FRAGMENTAL VOLCANIC ROCKS

Explosive volcanic eruptions give rise to many products; the **pyroclastic** rocks embrace fragments of different origins, many shapes, and all sizes. Some accumulations of volcanic debris are uniform in composition and texture; others are heterogeneous mixtures. Pyroclastic deposits include fragments of rocks shattered by explosions and materials derived from the rapid cooling of forcefully ejected lava.

The most violent explosions take place when increasing gas pressure finally succeeds in blasting a way through an obstruction of firm rock. In outbrusts of greatest intensity the barrier may be disintegrated to dust-size particles; on a more moderate scale the explosion produces an aggregate of angular blocks, a **volcanic breccia.** **Agglomerate** is the breccia formed in the throat of a volcano by the disruption of a thick solidified crust or hardened plug of lava. Blocks that have suffered only slight movement may fit together as a loose mosaic, otherwise they are completely disordered. Some agglomerates are cemented by irregular dikes and fillings of lava.

Most eruptions occur as renewed activity in a volcano already established. Hence the fragments consist mostly of rocks making up the plug or the sides of the volcano. When nonvolcanic fragments form an appreciable part of the debris, they point either to a volcano newly formed, or to fracturing along an easier way through the country rock. Occasional "foreign" rocks dispersed through a pyroclastic deposit indicate that they have been brought up by the magma from the walls at some lower level.

Lava, blown out of volcanoes as a liquid and hardened during its flight through the air, provides the great bulk of pyroclastic material. Most of the lava violently extruded is dispersed as fine droplets. These quickly congeal into angular particles of glass and subsequently settle as so-called **volcanic ash.** Frequently the ash is mixed with crystals formed before the explosion took place. The crystals may be either intact or broken.

Lava that is sufficiently viscous may be hurled upward as cohering clots and return to earth as **volcanic bombs.** These are rounded oval bodies, streamlined by air resistance. Many of them are spongy or cellular, with a tight nonporous crust surrounding a coarsely vesicluar interior (Figure 9). Similar bodies with diameters of less than three or four centimeters are called **lapilli.**

Bombs and large fragments accumulate near the vent from which they were extruded; volcanic ash may be transported many miles by the wind, and the finest particles may remain suspended indefinitely as atmospheric dust.

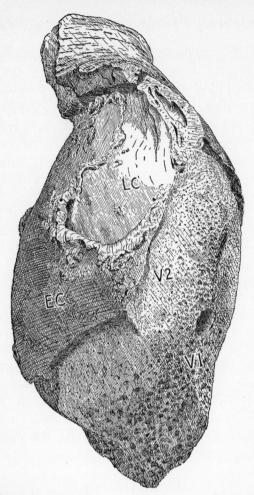

FIGURE 9. Volcanic bomb, approximately twelve inches long. The internal structure is visible to the right and below where the outer portion is broken away. The twisted and broken top end suggests that the original lava clot was irregularly shaped. The relatively slow cooling of the center is demonstrated by the large and closely spaced vesicles (V1). Nearer the edge the vesicles (V2) are smaller and more widely separated. Vesiculation increased the volume of the bomb and stretched the earlier crust (EC) to the breaking point. A later crust (LC) formed at the surface of the fluid lava thus exposed. Drawn by Paul Dobbs.

Tuff

Rocks consisting preponderantly of volcanic ash are called tuff. Commonly it occurs in well-defined layers, each one representing either a distinct fall of ash or a deposit carried downhill by water from the heavy rains that usually accompany volcanic activity. Explosions are often followed by flows of liquid lava, and therefore the flanks of many volcanoes are built of alternating layers of tuff and lava.

Newly fallen ash is a fine loose powder of gray or white particles that tend to cling because of their rough surfaces. Such aggregates are highly porous and readily admit air and water. The high porosity of ash beds, the fine texture, and the instability of glass, all facilitate weathering. Consequently, many tuffs acquire deep shades of red, brown, or yellow. Tuffs may be cemented or hardened by compaction, but they nevertheless tend to retain considerable pore space and therefore are rocks of low density.

Tuff that accumulates near the vent of a volcano is often a confused mixture of rock fragments and minerals held in a matrix of volcanic ash. The different response of these ingredients to weathering and to the chemical action of volcanic gases produces sharp color constrasts that emphasize the heterogeneous composition.

Volcanic ash that falls or is washed into a lake or the sea mingles with the products of local sedimentation. Descriptive names such as "tuffaceous limestone" and "tuffaceous shale" are used to designate their mixed compositon and dual origin.

APHANITIC ROCKS

Aphanitic igneous rocks occur as small intrusive bodies and as lava flows. Their identification in hand specimens is possible only when they exhibit characteristics sufficiently marked to be of diagnostic value. Some are so fine textured that the microscope fails to reveal all the minerals, and accurate classification calls for chemical analysis. Fortunately, however, a large percentage of aphanitic rocks are porphyritic, and the phenocrysts, even though they seldom serve to fix the rock within a narrow category, are valuable indicators of the limits of probable mineral composition.

Igneous Rocks

Most aphanitic rocks can be conveniently arranged in a sequence that runs approximately parallel to the granite-gabbro series of the phaneric intrusives. However, it is to be emphasized that the names used in both groups of rocks mark gradational changes that do not follow any single fixed course. Furthermore, it is not accurate to describe rhyolites as the aphanitic equivalent of granite. Even though the lava that produced the rhyolite may have resembled in many respects the magma that gave rise to the granite, the two rocks crystallize under very different conditions and at different rates. The disparity in temperature, pressure, viscosity, gas content, and other factors that control crystallization may lead not only to wide differences in the relative quantities of minerals but also to different mineral assemblages.

TABLE 5. Aphanitic Igneous Rocks

Aphanitic Rocks	Approximate Phaneric Counterparts
Rhyolite	Granite
Dacite	Granodiorite
	Quartz diorite
Andesite	Diorite
Basalt	Gabbro and dolerite
Trachyte	Syenite
Phonolite	Nepheline syenite
None	Anorthosite, pyroxenite, dunite, peridotite, serpentine

Of the aphanitic rocks listed in Table 5, **basalt** is by far the most common and the most abundant, whereas **phonolite, leucite basalt,** and **analcite basalt** are rare. There are no aphanitic rocks related to anorthosite, pyroxenite, dunite, or peridotite.

Phenocrysts are common in all the aphanitic rocks except basalt. In general they tend to be larger and more numerous in the hypabyssal rocks than in the lavas, but there are many exceptions. In the hand specimen it is possible to distinguish between intrusive and extrusive rocks only when the latter exhibit definite characteristics of lava, such as pronounced flow structure, vesiculation, or considerable amounts of glass. The lack of these features, however, does not indicate an intrusive rock.

Professor F. F. Grout has provided a useful and practicable system of nomenclature that should be employed for aphanitic rocks with phenocrysts whenever the field occurrence is known. The term *porphyry,* used as a noun, is applied only to intrusive rocks. Thus *rhyolite porphyry, andesite porphyry,* etc., are used to designate rocks of hypabyssal intrusions. Conversely rocks named *rhyolite, andesite, trachyte,* and so on, signify extrusive bodies. Hence a lava flow of appropriate composition and containing phenocrysts should be called *porphyritic dacite,* whereas *dacite porphyry* refers to an intrusive rock of similar composition.

Rhyolite and Quartz Porphyry

Rhyolite includes rocks diverse in texture, color, and structure, but related by a general similarity of chemical composition. Some are crystalline, others are glassy, and many are mixtures of glass and crystals. Nearly all obsidian, pitchstone, and pumice are rhyolites. Crystalline rhyolite consists of alkali feldspar and quartz, together with a minor amount of dark minerals. Rhyolite glasses have corresponding compositions.

The only minerals that can be identified are the phenocrysts, for the components of the aphanitic matrix are too fine to be resolved by a hand lens. The common phenocrysts are quartz and sanidine, a clear, glassy variety of orthoclase. By megascopic methods alone, it is impossible to identify a rock as rhyolite unless it contains visible quartz.

Flow structure is usually present and often conspicuous. The high viscosity of rhyolite lavas gives rise to curved, contorted lines and bands. Vesiculation is also common; it may appear as isolated cavities or convert the rock to a frothy pumice.

Except for obsidian and pitchstone, fresh rhyolite is gray or white, or takes a reddish shade from potash feldspar. Alteration greatly extends the range of colors. In addition to weathering, rhyolite is subject to the attack of gases. These may have been imprisoned in the congealing lava, or may emanate from a volcanic source. Weathering produces a characteristic iron oxide stain; hot gases convert the feldspars to a pastelike mixture with the consistency of chalk. This is usually white or gray, but may be faintly green from the destruction of iron-bearing silicates.

Intrusive rocks of rhyolitic composition differ from the lavas in several respects. They nearly all contain abundant phenocrysts, and these tend to be large and euhedral. Flow structures are seldom apparent. The matrix, even though aphanitic, appears less homogeneous, and in the larger intrusions is distinctly granular. If orthoclase and quartz phenocrysts occur together, the rock can be called **rhyolite porphyry.** If quartz is alone or accompanies feldspars that can not be identified, the rock should be described as **quartz porphyry.**

Basalt

Basalt is the most widely distributed lava. Also it is easily identified. The chemical composition of basalts and their physical properties are subject to fewer variations than other kinds of lava. The essential minerals of basalt are pyroxene and a calcic or intermediate plagioclase. Both in minerals and composition they closely resemble the gabbros and dolerites. Like their phaneric counterparts, many basalts contain olivine, but unless this mineral occurs as phenocrysts, its presence cannot be detected. The dark colored minerals make up approximately half the rock. Basaltic lava flows are aphanitic; if glass is present, it occurs as a relatively thin outer crust, or occupies spaces between crystals. Basaltic glass, **tachylyte,** rarely makes up an entire flow.

The distinguishing features of basalt are its color, dark green or gray that approaches black, its aphanitic texture, and its high density. Phenocrysts are not as prevalent as in other lavas, but if they do appear they may consist of olivine, pyroxene, or hornblende.

Although the great majority of basalts consist of the essential minerals already indicated, there are many related lavas containing appreciable quantities of less common minerals. Unless these appear as phenocrysts, as in **leucite basalt,** the rocks that contain them cannot be distinguished from "normal" basalt.

The textures of basaltic lavas and intrusions closely reflect the cooling history of the parent mass. Thus in a thick lava flow the texture may grade from a glassy surface, through a finely aphanitic zone to an almost phaneric interior. Similarly a dike may be a basalt at the edges and dolerite within.

Because, in general, its lava is less viscous, flow structures are less obvious in the interior of basalts than in rhyolites. However, the surface of basalt may be marked by twisted, ropy ridges called **pahoehoe.** This is brought about by fluid lava moving below a more viscous outer skin.

The vesiculation of basalt takes several forms. It may consist of globular cavities, equal in size and equally spaced, or the vesicles may be flattened and elongated in the direction of flow. More commonly it produces **scoria,** an irregularly porous substance, with rough surfaces, sharp edges, and the appearance of cinders from a furnace.

Basalt, because it is richer in iron compounds than rhyolite, is more susceptible to weathering. Consequently it may be changed to deep reds and browns by oxidation. Although basalt is less commonly altered by enclosed gases, vesicles and joint cavities within many basalts are filled with carbonates, silica minerals, and zeolites.

Dacites and Andesites

The dacites and andesites are aphanitic igneous rocks of intermediate composition and density, occupying a position between the rhyolites and basalts. Thus they are roughly analogous to the granodiorites, quartz diorites, and diorites of the granite-gabbro series. The feldspar is plagioclase, near andesine. The dark minerals are pyroxene and hornblende rather than biotite. They vary in amount, but in general they make up from twenty to forty per cent of the rock.

The distinction between them is that dacite contains quartz, and andesite is presumably free from this mineral. However, the chemical analyses of many "andesites" have demonstrated that most of them contain excess silica, probably as minute quartz crystals hidden in the matrix. Hence it appears that nearly all andesite should actually be classified as dacite.

Phenocrysts are common in both the lava flows and intrusions.

In many rocks they are large and euhedral, and in both dacites and andesites it is not unusual to find more than one mineral providing the phenocrysts. When this happens, each mineral may be limited to a distinct size range. The phenocrysts to be expected are feldspar, quartz, pyroxene, hornblende, and occasionally biotite.

An aphanitic dacite or andesite, free from phenocrysts and unaltered, is usually gray or a gray-green in color, seldom as dark as basalt or as light as rhyolite. It appears homogeneous and dull. The intermediate color is explained by the amount of iron-bearing minerals. Phenocrysts give many of these rocks a striking appearance. The crystallization of feldspar or quartz segregates a large quantity of the light colored components in the phenocrysts, and thereby enriches the matrix in iron-magnesium compounds. Thus a sharp contrast prevails between the light phenocrysts and dark groundmass. Conversely, when hornblende or pyroxene provide the phenocrysts, they appear dark against a lighter background.

These rocks are readily altered by hot gases, especially water vapor. Frequently iron-bearing silicates are changed to chlorite which gives the rock a deep green color. Intense alteration renders them soft and pasty.

Trachyte and Phonolite

Trachyte is the approximate equivalent of syenite. Phonolite bears the same relationship to nepheline syenite. Neither is a common rock. Both consist predominantly of light colored minerals; alkali feldspar is the chief constituent of trachyte, and most phonolites consist of alkali feldspar, with either nepheline or leucite.

If phenocrysts occur in trachyte, they are usually feldspars—sanidine in the lava flows, orthoclase or microcline in the intrusions. The feldspar in the matrix often crystallizes as long narrow laths. When these are drawn into subparallel alignments by flowing lava, typical **trachytic** structure ensues, a feature that is also common in andesites and basalts. Even though the individual crystals are invisible in hand specimens, their arrangement is reflected by an inconspicuous banding or streaking.

Trachyte can never be identified in hand specimens, and the only phonolite that can be distinguished megascopically is **leucite phono-**

lite, if the leucite crystals are big enough to see. This limitation seriously curtails the identification of aphanitic rocks, for the name given to a specimen implies the existence of certain critical minerals. Thus a rock with visible quartz may be either rhyolite or dacite. If sanidine is present in addition, the rock is probably rhyolite. On the other hand, if pyroxene or hornblende make up more than fifteen or twenty per cent, it would be closer to dacite. When these dark minerals are present in abundance and are recognizable, the rock may be either andesite or dacite, for the *absence of quartz cannot be established*. Furthermore this same rock could also be a phonolite. A rock with sanidine, but no other phenocrysts of diagnostic value, might be rhyolite, trachyte, or phonolite. Unless phenocrysts are present, the color of an aphanitic rock provides little information. Even among fresh rocks, both rhyolites and trachytes may be darker than some andesites. Basalt is the only exception, but in it the dark color is accompanied by its typically high specific gravity. A rock that yields insufficient information to justify a name should be described to indicate the probable limits of its composition.

Inclusions in Lava

Lava may lift and carry loose material from the ground, but most of the inclusions are fragments of the lava's own crust. In a slowly

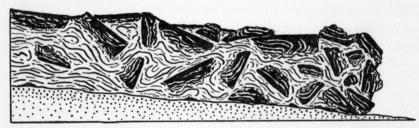

FIGURE 10. Outer edge of lava flow crowded with fragments of frozen crust.

moving lava, the liquid travels forward below a solidified cover. If, for any reason, this crust is broken, the resulting fragments are engulfed in the underlying liquid. Under these circumstances the number of fragments increases toward the forward edge of the flow. Hence many lavas that advance slowly present steep fronts, consisting of jagged and angular blocks with a minimum of liquid (Figure 10). Such a mixture moves with difficulty, for the fragments retard the rate of flow. The angular blocks constitute a breccia in which the cementing material is congealed lava. As evidence of the history of the mixed accumulation, the individual blocks display irregular, angular shapes, and signs of rapid hardening, such as vesicular cavities and selvages of glass.

SUGGESTIONS FOR STUDY

With experience, some rocks can be identified at a glance, just as many familiar objects can be recognized without detailed analysis. Skill in rapid sight identification is nevertheless not an end in itself, even though it is an encouraging sign of progress, for just as the easy recollection of the names and faces of casual acquaintances is a useful accomplishment, it brings no proficiency in estimating their characters or their places in the community. The following procedures are suggested as typical exercises to illustrate differences within related rock types and to cultivate care in observation.

1. Because of its abundance and its place in the architecture of continents, granite may be regarded as the most important rock type. Also its properties are so diverse that although two granites from separate intrusions may be superficially alike, they never have quite the same appearance. This provides a simple test for skill in observation and description. From a collection of granites (from ten to thirty), similar in color and texture, but all from different localities, the description of any specimen, made by one student, should be an adequate guide for another student to select the same rock.
2. Variations in texture, apart from wide mineralogical differences, can be demonstrated by arranging representative specimens of gabbro, dolerite, and basalt in order of increasing grain size. This alignment will show whether or not there is a definite point at which feldspar ceases to be recognizable, whether a sharp division can be made between aphanitic and phaneric rocks in this group and the relationship between texture and apparent (megascopic) homogeneity.
3. It is profitable to compare quartz, the feldspars, and the femic minerals in rocks of approximately equal grain size, ranging from granite through quartz diorite. The minerals should be examined for abundance, general appearance, shape, and mutual relationships.

4. Similar exercises will serve to call attention to: primary flow structures; the shapes, sizes, and ordering of phenocrysts; structures peculiar to the glasses and their devitrification.
5. From a miscellaneous assortment of lavas and hypabyssal rocks, both with and without phenocrysts, it is possible to separate some that are clearly effusive, and others that are intrusive, from those that are indeterminate without field evidence. This exercise is useful in drawing up lists of criteria for recognizing the contrasted modes of occurrence.

.5.

The Composition of Igneous Rocks

AN IGNEOUS rock comes into existence and acquires its specifie characteristics through the operation of both chemical and physical changes. These depend upon the properties of the lava or magma and the influence of the environment under which it erupts and cools. Of the many variables that control the behavior of igneous liquids, a large number are interdependent. For example, the size of crystals depends partly upon the composition of the magma and partly upon the rate at which crystals are formed. The rate of crystallization, in turn, is determined by composition and viscosity, and viscosity is a function of both composition and temperature. It will be clear that liquids of different composition will produce different minerals, regardless of the local environment. It is significant also, that similar liquids, crystallizing under different conditions, will vary, not only in texture but also in mineralogy. Hence it follows that an understanding of rocks and of the minerals of rocks must be based on a broad acquaintance with all the factors that can be known about them. Without an appreciation of their composition and the chemical processes that are involved, no attempt can be made to account for their diversity, their origin, or the subsequent changes by which they are modified.

Rock-Forming Elements

In igneous rocks, only eleven elements are quantitatively important and make up over ninety-nine per cent of all igneous matter.

71

These are, in order of abundance: oxygen, silicon, aluminum, iron, calcium, sodium, potassium, magnesium, titanium, phosphorus, and hydrogen. Two less common elements, carbon and sulfur, are added to the list because of the wide distribution and significance of their compounds in rocks of other origins.

Oxygen accounts for nearly half the weight of igneous rocks, and appears in all the essential minerals. These compounds are silicates*

TABLE 6.　Composition of the Average Igneous Rock
(From U.S.G.S. Bulletin 770)

Elements		Oxides	
O	46.42	SiO_2	59.14
Si	27.59	Al_2O_3	15.34
Al	8.08	Fe_2O_3	3.08
Fe	5.08	FeO	3.80
Ca	3.61	MgO	3.49
Na	2.83	CaO	5.08
K	2.58	Na_2O	3.84
Mg	2.09	K_2O	3.13
Ti	0.721	H_2O	1.15
P	0.158	TiO_2	1.05
H	0.130	CO_2	0.101
S	0.080	S	0.052
C	0.051	P_2O_5	0.299
Others	0.58	Others	0.448
	100.		100.

and oxides. Since the proportions of oxygen to the other rock-forming elements are fixed by the valences of the latter, it is convenient to report the compositions of rocks and of many minerals in terms of oxides rather than elements. Table 6 presents the composition of the *average igneous rock* as computed by the late Dr. F. W. Clarke. In this table the composition is given by both methods. The elements are listed in order of decreasing abundance; the oxides are arranged in the order that follows the standard usage of the U.S. Geological Survey for rock analyses. Among the oxides, it will be

* Until recently, quartz was considered an oxide. Modern mineralogists include it with the silicates because the arrangement of silicon and oxygen ions follows a similar basic pattern in all crystals that contain these elements.

observed that iron occurs in both trivalent and bivalent forms. These are called *ferric oxide* and *ferrous oxide* respectively. The names of the other oxides, together with their formulas and molecular weights, and also the symbols, atomic numbers, and atomic weights of the elements are given in Table 7.

TABLE 7. Chemical Components of Igneous Rocks
(The atomic and molecular weights are given to the nearest whole number)

Atomic No.	Element	Symbol	Atomic Wt.	Oxide	Formula	Mol. Wt.
8	Oxygen	O	16	Silica	SiO_2	60
14	Silicon	Si	28	Alumina	Al_2O_3	102
13	Aluminum	Al	27	Ferric oxide	Fe_2O_3	160
26	Iron	Fe	56	Ferrous oxide	FeO	72
12	Magnesium	Mg	24	Magnesia	MgO	40
20	Calcium	Ca	40	Lime	CaO	56
11	Sodium	Na	23	Soda	Na_2O	62
19	Potassium	K	39	Potash	K_2O	94
1	Hydrogen	H	1	Water	H_2O	18
22	Titanium	Ti	48	Titania	TiO_2	80
6	Carbon	C	12	Carbon dioxide	CO_2	44

IGNEOUS ROCK MINERALS

Except for quartz, which is invariably silicon dioxide, SiO_2, few minerals important in igneous rocks have compositions that can be expressed by a simple empirical formula. Most feldspars, pyroxenes, amphiboles, and micas are complex compounds, subject to wide variations in composition. The three-dimensional arrangements of their crystalline structures permit the substitution of certain ions, at definite points within their space lattices, for other ions having the same approximate sizes. In some minerals, one ion may be substituted for another throughout the entire crystal, in others the amount of substitution is limited, and may differ for different temperatures. Some minerals are able to entertain ions of several elements. Considering chemical composition rather than the physical structure of crystals, the minerals that contain several different kinds of ions may be regarded as complex compounds in which the ingredients are other compounds of simpler composition. The feldspar group provides the best example to illustrate compositional variation, and the corresponding effects upon the physical properties that such variation entails.

The Feldspar Group

The feldspars consist of combinations of three *end members* which seldom exist in a pure state. The names, compositions,* and specific gravities of these are:

Potash feldspar	$KAlSi_3O_8$	or	$K_2O \cdot Al_2O_3 \cdot 6SiO_2$	2.56
Albite	$NaAlSi_3O_8$		$Na_2O \cdot Al_2O_3 \cdot 6SiO_2$	2.62
Anorthite	$CaAl_2Si_2O_8$		$CaO \cdot Al_2O_3 \cdot 2SiO_2$	2.76

The potash feldspars are orthoclase, including sanidine, and microcline. In igneous rocks they may be expected to contain the other end members; albite may be included up to a maximum of thirty per cent; the anorthite content is much lower, usually less than five per cent. Albite and anorthite are the end members of the plagioclase group, with minerals of all intermediate compositions providing a complete isomorphous series of homogeneous crystals. Their densities, cleavage angles, and optical properties are directly related to composition. If the composition of a plagioclase is known, it is indicated in abbreviated form thus: $Ab_{60}An_{40}$, or $Ab_{10}An_{90}$, to show the percentages of albite and anorthite respectively. This notation, however, fails to take account of the potash feldspar which is commonly present in the plagioclase of normal igneous rocks. Plagioclase near the albite end of the series may contain up to thirty per cent of potash feldspar; those rich in anorthite have less than ten per cent. The terms albite and anorthite are used in two senses; for the chemical composition of the end members, Ab and An, and for the actual plagioclases that contain not less than ninety per cent of these. Usually the context will make clear the use that is intended. The study of hand specimens does not reveal the potash feldspar in plagioclase, nor the plagioclase concealed in orthoclase or sanidine, however their presence can often be inferred from the chemical analyses of rocks.

* In stating the compositions of potash feldspar and albite in oxides, it is necessary to double the formulas in the adjacent column, but the proportions remain unchanged.

The Composition of Igneous Rocks

Pyroxenes and Hornblende

The pyroxenes include a large number of minerals. Of these, a few are relatively simple compounds, but augite, which is the most common, is both complex and variable. A generalized formula for the pyroxene group is $RSiO_3$. In the pyroxene of common igneous rocks, the R signifies magnesium, usually with the addition of calcium and iron. Thus diopside is approximately $MgCa(SiO_3)_2$, but it usually contains enough iron to be distinctly green. Augite contains all these elements and also aluminum, ferric iron, and sometimes titanium. Rocks rich in alkalies may contain soda-bearing augite, and other soda-pyroxenes. The composition of an augite can be established only by chemical analysis, and when this is obtained, the chance that it will match the analysis of an augite from some other locality is exceedingly small. The formula for an augite, computed from a chemical analysis, is no less cumbersome than the analysis expressed in terms of the percentages of oxides of elements.

The composition of hornblende is similar to that of augite. It contains variable amounts of the same elements, but with hydrogen in addition.

The Micas

Pure muscovite has the formula $H_2KAl_3Si_3O_8$, or in oxides; $2H_2O \cdot K_2O \cdot 3Al_2O_3 \cdot 6SiO_2$. In phlogopite the proportions remain the same, but magnesium is substituted for some of the aluminum. Biotite is highly variable with iron and magnesium taking the place of aluminum and silicon ions.

Olivine

The olivines form an isomorphous series with Mg_2SiO_4 and Fe_2SiO_4 as the end members. In the olivines of igneous rocks the magnesium is considerably in excess of the iron. The ratio of silica to metallic oxides is lower in olivine than in pyroxene, thus:

Olivine	$(Mg, Fe)_2SiO_4$	or	$2(Mg, Fe)O \cdot SiO_2$
Pyroxene	$MgSiO_3$		$MgO \cdot SiO_2$

Olivine appears in rocks only if the available silica is insufficient to form pyroxene, and hence its presence marks a rock as deficient in silica. Similarly olivine is not to be expected in association with quartz, for quartz is crystallized when the silica is in excess of the amount needed to combine with the various metallic elements. With this concept in view, olivine and other minerals that are produced in igneous rocks when there is not enough silica to meet the requirements of the metallic ions, are called **unsaturated** minerals. The rocks that contain them are **undersaturated** rocks. This terminology was introduced by Professor S. J. Shand and is widely used. **Oversaturated** rocks are those which contain quartz; **saturated** rocks contain neither quartz nor unsaturated minerals.

Nepheline and Leucite

Nepheline and leucite contain the same elements as albite and potash feldspar respectively. However they contain less silica, and hence are unsaturated minerals. Nepheline has the composition $NaAlSiO_4$, but may have a small amount of potassium taking the place of part of the sodium. Calcium may also be present. The compositions of nepheline and albite are more readily compared when the formulas are written as oxides:

Nepheline	$Na_2O \cdot Al_2O_3 \cdot 2SiO_2$
Albite	$Na_2O \cdot Al_2O_3 \cdot 6SiO_2$

Leucite is $KAlSi_2O_6$, differing from potash feldspar thus:

Leucite	$K_2O \cdot Al_2O_3 \cdot 4SiO_2$
Potash feldspar	$K_2O \cdot Al_2O_3 \cdot 6SiO_2$

During the crystallization of igneous rocks, silica combines with aluminum and the other elements to form feldspar to the extent that it is available. When a shortage of silica requires the presence of nepheline or leucite (sometimes both), it is seldom so serious as to exclude the alkali feldspars completely. Unsaturated minerals in general crystallize only in the quantity demanded by the ratio of silica to the other ingredients. Nepheline and leucite, like olivine, do not appear with quartz for the same reason.

Other Rock-Forming Minerals

Table 8 lists the compositions and specific gravities of minerals that may occur in appreciable quantities in the common rocks. The

TABLE 8. Composition of the Rock-Forming Minerals
(Data from Clarke, Dana, Hurlbut, Winchell, etc.)

Mineral	Formula	As Oxides	Mol. Wt.	S.G.
Quartz	SiO_2	SiO_2	60	2.65
Potash feldspar	$KAlSi_3O_8$	$K_2O \cdot Al_2O_3 \cdot 6SiO_2$	556	2.56
Albite	$NaAlSi_3O_8$	$Na_2O \cdot Al_2O_3 \cdot 6SiO_2$	524	2.62
Anorthite	$CaAl_2Si_2O_8$	$CaO \cdot Al_2O_3 \cdot 2SiO_2$	278	2.76
Diopside	$CaMgSi_2O_6$	$CaO \cdot MgO \cdot 2SiO_2$	216	3.3
Augite	$RSiO_3$ with Mg, Fe, Ca, Al, $\pm$ Ti, Na		—	3.3
Hornblende	similar to augite but including OH		—	3.2
Muscovite	$H_2KAl_3Si_3O_{12}$	$2H_2O \cdot K_2O \cdot 3Al_2O_3 \cdot 6SiO_2$	796	2.8
Phlogopite	$H_2KMg_2AlSi_3O_{12}$	$2H_2O \cdot K_2O \cdot 4MgO \cdot Al_2O_3 \cdot 6SiO_2$	752	2.9
Biotite	similar to phlogopite but containing iron		—	3$\pm$
Olivine	$(Mg, Fe)_2SiO_4$	$2(Mg, Fe)O \cdot SiO_2$	—	3.3
Nepheline	$NaAlSiO_4$	$Na_2O \cdot Al_2O_3 \cdot 2SiO_2$	284	2.6
Leucite	$KAlSi_2O_6$	$K_2O \cdot Al_2O_3 \cdot 4SiO_2$	436	2.5
Magnetite	Fe_3O_4	$FeO \cdot Fe_2O_3$	232	5.2
Ilmenite	$FeTiO_3$	$FeO \cdot TiO_2$	152	4.7
Pyrite	FeS_2	———	120	5.0
Calcite	$CaCO_3$	$CaO \cdot CO_2$	100	2.72
Dolomite	$CaMg(CO_3)_2$	$CaO \cdot MgO \cdot 2CO_2$	184	2.9
Siderite	$FeCO_3$	$FeO \cdot CO_2$	116	3.9
Chalcedony	SiO_2	SiO_2	60	2.6
Opal	$SiO_2 \cdot nH_2O$	$SiO_2 \cdot nH_2O$	—	2.1$\pm$
Hematite	Fe_2O_3	Fe_2O_3	160	5.3
Limonite	$FeO \cdot OH$	$Fe_2O_3 \cdot H_2O$	178	4.3
Kaolinite	$H_4Al_2Si_2O_9$	$2H_2O \cdot Al_2O_3 \cdot 2SiO_2$	258	2.6
Gypsum	$CaSO_4 \cdot 2H_2O$	$2H_2O \cdot CaO \cdot SO_3$	172	2.3
Anhydrite	$CaSO_4$	$CaO \cdot SO_3$	136	2.9
Garnet	$R''_3R'''_2Si_3O_{12}$	$3RO \cdot R_2O_3 \cdot 3SiO_2$	—	—
Grossularite	$Ca_3Al_2Si_3O_{12}$	$3CaO \cdot Al_2O_3 \cdot 3SiO_2$	450	3.5
Andradite	$Ca_3Fe_2Si_3O_{12}$	$3CaO \cdot Fe_2O_3 \cdot 3SiO_2$	508	3.8
Almandite	$Fe_3Al_2Si_3O_{12}$	$3FeO \cdot Al_2O_3 \cdot 3SiO_2$	498	4.3
Chlorite*	$H_8(Mg, Fe)_5Al_2Si_3O_{18}$	$4H_2O \cdot 5(Mg, Fe)O \cdot Al_2O_3 \cdot 3SiO_2$	—	2.8$\pm$
Talc	$H_2Mg_3Si_4O_{12}$	$H_2O \cdot 3MgO \cdot 4SiO_2$	378	2.8$\pm$
Serpentine	$H_4Mg_3Si_2O_9$	$2H_2O \cdot 3MgO \cdot 2SiO_2$	276	2.6$\pm$
Epidote*	$HCa_2(Al, Fe)_3Si_3O_{13}$	$H_2O \cdot 4CaO \cdot 3(Al, Fe)_2O_3 \cdot 6SiO_2$	—	3.4
Glauconite	variable $KFe'''Si_2O_6$ with other bases and water		—	2.3
Kyanite	Al_2SiO_5	$Al_2O_3 \cdot SiO_2$	162	3.6
Andalusite	Al_2SiO_5	$Al_2O_3 \cdot SiO_2$	162	3.2
Staurolite	$HFeAl_5Si_2O_{13}$	$H_2O \cdot 2FeO \cdot 5Al_2O_3 \cdot 4SiO_2$	912	3.7

* See text.

order of listing is without significance, but the minerals of the igneous rocks are given precedence. Many accessory minerals that are widely distributed have been excluded, because in ordinary rocks their crystals are too small to be seen (zircon, sphene, apatite). Also minerals that are peculiar to pegmatites, veins, and ore bodies have been omitted.

Calcite, dolomite, and siderite are the rock-forming members of a large isomorphous group that embraces many other minerals. Similarly, only three varieties of garnet are listed. Neither chlorite nor epidote is a distinct mineral, but rather a group name used to include a wide range of complex compounds. Consequently the formulas assigned to them are necessarily simplified. The many separate minerals that constitute the clays can be identified only by refined laboratory methods. Of these, kaolinite is the best known, and it is used here to represent the entire group. Limonite includes several hydrated iron oxides, and a single specimen is commonly a mixture of these. The composition is that of goethite.

The molecular weights refer to the formulas expressed as oxides and are based on atomic weights taken to the nearest whole number. Specific gravities are given to two figures only, except those of a few minerals with fixed densities that are used as standards of comparison. Intermediate values are assigned to minerals having a wide range of specific gravities.

CHEMICAL COMPOSITION OF THE IGNEOUS ROCKS

The chemical analysis of a rock presents each oxide as its weight per cent. Except in particularly refined analyses, the minor constituents and trace elements are disregarded. Rock analyses serve several ends. In the specific study of a rock or group of rocks, the chief use is to supplement the information obtained in other ways. Without chemical analyses it is impossible to make a precise identification of glasses or of aphanitic rocks with crystals too small to be resolved by the microscope. Analyses also reveal chemical similarities and differences that may not be evident from a comparison of minerals alone. A general familiarity with the composition of the different kinds of igneous rock is an absolute prerequisite to any attempt to explain their origin, or to understand magmas and lavas and the laws that govern their solidification.

If the minerals of rock can be identified and their quantities measured or approximated, these data can be used to make a rough estimate of the composition, for the make-up of a rock is necessarily the sum of its components. On the other hand, it is impossible to determine the character of a rock from a chemical analysis alone, since rocks of closely related composition may differ in origin, as well as in texture and mineralogy. However, when the details of a rock can be observed, the chemical analysis permits the rendering of a more completely quantitative account. Similarly, rock analyses provide for a reasonable interpretation of the features obscured by aphanitic texture or alteration.

The study of the chemical composition of a rock çan never be divorced from a consideration of its composition in terms of minerals. Each constituent represents a contribution to one or more of the minerals present. The tentative assignment of the oxides among the appropriate minerals is greatly facilitated by the limited number of minerals that may be expected in igneous rocks of the same kind; it becomes an almost automatic procedure after a few analyses have been compared. The following list indicates the distribution of oxides among the abundant igneous rock minerals; it is a qualitative rearrangement of the data in the first part of Table 8.

Silica	Alone as quartz and combined with other elements in all the common minerals except the metallic oxides and some accessories
Alumina	Feldspars, feldspathoids, micas, sparingly present in augite and hornblende
Iron oxide	Magnetite, ilmenite, and all dark silicates; augite, hornblende, biotite, olivine
Magnesia	Augite, hornblende, biotite, phlogopite, olivine
Lime	Plagioclase (anorthite end member), augite, hornblende
Soda	Plagioclase (albite end member), nepheline, soda-rich amphiboles and pyroxenes
Potash	Potash feldspar, mica, leucite
Water	Mica, hornblende, also in many alteration products
Titania	Ilmenite, sparingly in some augite and hornblende, otherwise in accessories

The significance of the various oxides shown in a chemical analysis lies partly in their absolute amounts and partly in their relative quantities. For example, a rock with a high percentage of silica may be expected to contain quartz, its amount depending upon the silica requirements of the other substances that combine to form silicates. In a hypothetical rock consisting of quartz, the three feldspar end members, and magnetite, the chemical composition would fix the amount of each compound. The two iron oxides would be united as magnetite, and their sum would be the per cent of magnetite in the rock. The weight of potash would determine the amount of silica required for potash feldspar, and the weights of soda and lime would call for appropriate quantities of silica for albite and anorthite respectively. The alumina would be distributed between the three feldspars in their required ratios and would provide a check on the allotment of the other oxides. The silica that remains after subtracting the amounts needed for feldspar would represent the amount of quartz.

In the foregoing example the correspondence is between chemical composition and combinations of oxides, but not between composition and actual minerals. The amount of magnetite is fixed exactly and the quartz within narrow limits, but the feldspars present several alternatives. Even in a hypothetical rock there can be no justification for the coexistence of albite and anorthite. These two end members will combine to form a plagioclase, but not necessarily the one indicated by the ratio of soda to lime. Unless the amount of potash feldspar is insignificant, it may include an appreciable quantity of soda feldspar and a smaller part of lime. Similarly the plagioclase may contain potash feldspar, and if it is a sodic variety, it may conceal some or all of the potash that would otherwise appear as orthoclase or microcline.

Nevertheless, chemical composition governs many of the characteristics of a rock even though it does not determine the precise mineral composition. The total amount of magnesia, iron oxides, and titania indicates the approximate color and density by controlling the quantity of dark minerals. Alumina provides a rough index to the amount of feldspar, and the alkalies and lime suggest the distribution among the feldspars of the three end members. If a rock contains a large amount of quartz or of unsaturated minerals, their presence can usually be determined from the analysis, but it will not reveal these minerals if they constitute only a small fraction of the rock.

Familiarity with typical analyses of the various igneous rocks such as granite, quartz diorite, and so on, leads to a general understanding of the ranges through which their compositions may vary. When this has been achieved, a rock can be approximately classified if at least some of the minerals are sufficiently fresh, or coarse enough for identification.

Because the chemical composition of every igneous rock is unique, no single analysis can be selected as typical and so be used to represent the group in which it is classified. However, Professor Daly has computed the *average* chemical compositions of all the types of igneous rocks that are significant in petrology. These averages illustrate the similarities and differences among the various kinds of rocks, and they provide standards for the comparison of specific analyses. Such a comparison will reveal immediately in which constituents a particular rock is rich or deficient and provides a quantitative measure of their departure from the average. The range of chemical compositions that may occur within a group of highly diversified rocks, such as the granites, can be appreciated only by examining a great number of analyses. It cannot be inferred from these average compositions. Table 9 reproduces the average analyses* of the most common rocks and of a few others that are important though relatively rare.

The chemical relationships between rocks known or presumed to be genetically related are most easily examined when the constituents are plotted on a **variation diagram.** These are simple graphs showing the per cent by weight of the various oxides. Since silica is the most important of these and almost invariably the most abundant, the silica content is used as the horizontal coordinate, and the position of each analysis on the x-axis is thus fixed by its silica percentage. The other constituents are then plotted at their appropriate

* In this table the oxides have been rearranged to conform with the standard usage of the U.S. Geological Survey, also the MnO has been included with the FeO. The specific gravities are given to three figures instead of four.

TABLE 9. Average Compositions of Igneous Rocks

Intrusive Rocks

	Granite	Granodiorite	Quartz diorite	Diorite	Gabbro	Syenite	Nepheline syenite	Anorthosite	Pyroxenite	Dunite	Peridotite (Lherzolite)	Peridotite** (Kimberlite)
SiO_2	70.18	65.01	61.59	56.77	48.24	60.19	54.63	50.40	52.33	40.49	43.95	34.73
Al_2O_3	14.47	15.94	16.21	16.67	17.88	16.28	19.89	28.30	3.54	.86	4.82	2.88
Fe_2O_3	1.57	1.74	2.54	3.16	3.16	2.74	3.37	1.06	2.61	2.84	2.20	6.10
FeO^*	1.90	2.72	3.87	4.53	6.08	3.42	2.55	1.17	5.34	5.70	6.53	3.13
MgO	.88	1.91	2.80	4.17	7.51	2.49	.87	1.25	23.92	46.32	36.81	31.41
CaO	1.99	4.42	5.38	6.74	10.99	4.30	2.51	12.46	10.29	.70	3.57	5.79
Na_2O	3.48	3.70	3.37	3.39	2.55	3.98	8.26	3.67	.43	.10	.63	.33
K_2O	4.11	2.75	2.10	2.12	.89	4.49	5.46	.74	.35	.04	.21	1.17
H_2O	.84	1.04	1.22	1.36	1.45	1.16	1.35	.75	1.03	2.88	1.08	9.20
TiO_2	.39	.57	.66	.84	.97	.67	.86	.15	.10	.02	.10	1.62
P_2O_5	.19	.20	.26	.25	.28	.28	.25	.05	.06	.05	.10	1.06
S.G.	2.67	2.72	2.75	2.87	2.98	2.73	2.61	2.75	3.32	3.29	3.33	—

82

Extrusive Rocks

	Rhyolite	Dacite	Andesite	Basalt	Trachyte	Phonolite
SiO_2	72.80	65.68	59.59	49.06	60.68	57.45
Al_2O_3	13.49	16.25	17.31	15.70	17.74	20.60
Fe_2O_3	1.45	2.38	3.33	5.38	2.64	2.35
$FeO*$	.96	1.96	3.31	6.68	2.68	1.16
MgO	.38	1.41	2.75	6.17	1.12	.30
CaO	1.20	3.46	5.80	8.95	3.09	1.50
Na_2O	3.38	3.97	3.58	3.11	4.43	8.84
K_2O	4.46	2.67	2.04	1.52	5.74	5.23
H_2O	1.47	1.50	1.26	1.62	1.26	2.04
TiO_2	.33	.57	.77	1.36	.38	.41
P_2O_5	.08	.15	.26	.45	.24	.12

Note: Data reproduced from *Igneous Rocks and the Depths of the Earth* by R. A. Daly, 1933. Courtesy of the McGraw-Hill Book Company.
 * Figures for FeO include MnO.
** CO_2 2.58%.

83

distances above these points and are connected by curves. Figure 11 is a variation diagram for the comparison of the average compositions of granite, granodiorite, the diorites, and gabbro. Even though the curves have not been smoothed, the diagram shows clearly the

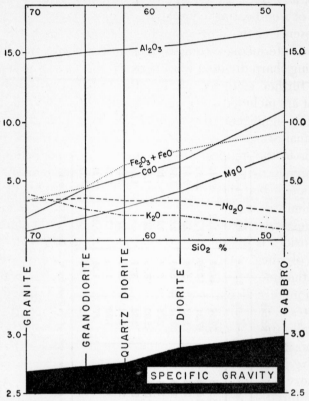

FIGURE 11.   Average compositions and densities of the most common phaneric rocks.

regularity of the change in composition from one rock to the next. Also it illustrates the necessary correlation between chemical and mineral composition. Thus the curves of magnesia and the iron oxides rise toward gabbro, as the silica diminishes and the femic minerals increase. Similarly the change in the feldspars is reflected by the change in the downward slope of potash, marking a decrease in the potash feldspar end member and the rise of lime accompanying the increase of anorthite. Average specific gravities for these rocks are shown graphically in the lower part of Figure 11. The ascent of the curve from left to right follows from the decrease and disappearance of quartz and the diminishing quantities of alkali feldspars, and from the change to more calcic feldspar and larger amounts of iron-bearing minerals.

The absence of sharp breaks in the diagram suggests the existence of rocks of intermediate compositions and indicates the difficulty of establishing sharp dividing lines between the various groups. Also it presents further evidence of the close relationships between the rocks that are included and points toward a hypothesis of a common origin. It is significant that none of the other phaneric rocks with average analyses given in Table 9 fits the curves made by this series. This leads to the implication that the syenites, nepheline syenites, and ultrafemic rocks have either formed from magmas of different composition or that their crystallization follows a different course.

The chemistry of the syenites is characterized by large amounts of the alkalies and relatively high lime and alumina. The greater part of these oxides is present in the feldspar. In most syenites the percentages of silica, magnesia, and the iron oxides are intermediate between the amounts in granite and gabbro. Nepheline syenites contain even more soda and potash, but less lime. Also they differ from the syenites in containing less silica. It is this deficiency that leads to the crystallization of unsaturated minerals.

Anorthosite is rich only in alumina and lime, which with silica and soda are required for plagioclase. The other constituents occur only in accessory minerals.

All the ultrafemic rocks are marked by large quantities of magnesia and minor amounts of alumina and the alkalies. This is to be expected from the virtual absence of feldspar and the preponderance of minerals such as pyroxene and olivine. It is noteworthy that in the four average analyses of these rocks in Table 9, the magnesia is several times larger than that of the combined iron oxides. This relationship holds true in all ultrafemic rocks except a few that consist mostly of metallic oxides.

The chemistry of extrusive rocks approximates closely the composition of their nearest intrusive equivalents. A minor but consistent difference is the slightly higher silica content of the aphanitic rocks. This may result partly from the more rapid cooling, which tends to prevent the escape of silica-bearing fluids. Another explanation lies in the difficulty of identifying finely divided silica minerals in the aphanatic groundmass; a rock with silica so concealed will often be called andesite rather than dacite.

SUGGESTIONS FOR STUDY

A general knowledge of the chemical composition of igneous rocks is necessary: (a) to understand the theories concerning their origin, (b) to examine their mutual relationships, and (c) to follow their reorganization by weathering and metamorphism. The chemical analysis of a rock is a difficult and complicated task usually reserved for the specialist, but it is relatively simple to acquire a sufficient, though vicarious, background of information: (a) by computing theoretical compositions from known or assumed mineral aggregates, and (b) by examining and comparing published analyses.

1. The first step is to practice converting the chemical formulas of rock-forming minerals into composition in terms of oxides. The slide rule will save time in these computations and appropriately limit the results to not more than three significant figures. In the computation of the composition of potash feldspar, shown below as an example, the formula is stated in oxides, $K_2O \cdot Al_2O_3 \cdot 6SiO_2$, rather than by the conventional method.

Oxide	Mol. wt.	To 100%
K_2O	94	16.9
Al_2O_3	102	18.4
$6SiO_2$	360	64.7
	556	100.0

The other common minerals of the igneous rocks should be similarly converted to the percentage weights of their constituent oxides. For highly variable minerals such as biotite, hornblende, and augite, it will be necessary to assign fixed and arbitrary formulas.

2. When the compositions of the rock-forming minerals have been tabulated for easy reference, they can be used to compute the chemical compositions of hypothetical rocks or to attempt approximations of the compositions of actual specimens in which the percentages of the different minerals have been determined. Thus in a rock containing forty

per cent of potash feldspar, by weight, this mineral would contribute forty per cent of the amounts of each of the three oxides as given in the example above.

3. In determining the abundance of minerals in a rock, the amounts are measured or estimated as percentage by volume. The method of converting volume percentage to per cent by weight and the reverse operation are shown in Appendix B.

4. Familiarity with the chemistry of the various rock types is acquired by examining and comparing the tabulated results of analyses. For this purpose an excellent general source is *The Data of Geochemistry*, by the late F. W. Clarke, U.S.G.S. Bulletin 770, 1924. This publication contains tables of analyses of sedimentary and metamorphic, as well as igneous, rocks and of many other earth materials in addition.

.6.

Petrogenesis of the Igneous Rocks

The history of an igneous rock involves a long sequence of events, of chemical and physical changes that are closely interrelated. The only igneous processes that can be observed directly are those that occur during surface eruptions. Information concerning the behavior of magma within the earth can be obtained only by indirect methods; the interpretation of the minerals, textures, and structures of igneous rocks, the interpretation of the changes within the adjacent wall rocks and through laboratory investigations of "artificial" magmas. Through these techniques, a vast amount of data has become available concerning the crystallization of rocks, even though petrologists differ in their interpretations of the evidence presented by igneous rocks and their hosts and disagree as to the significance of the laboratory experiments. The earliest step in igneous history is the generation of magma. This takes place so far below the surface that any hypotheses developed to account for its origin must rest as yet upon assumed conditions of temperature and pressure and deal with matter in a state inferred to exist under these conditions.

MAGMA

Within the magma are included all the constituents of igneous rocks that are usually stated in chemical analyses, together with a larger number of substances present in such minute quantities that they are detected only when special analytical methods are employed. The magma is a solution of its various components, but un-

88

like the usual solution of the chemical laboratory, in which one part is designated as the solvent and the remainder the solute, the magma is a mutual solution. This means that each substance is to be considered as dissolving the others, and at the same time being held in solution by them.

Among the ingredients of the magma, it is convenient to distinguish between the rock-forming components, those that crystallize as the usual igneous minerals, and a second fraction consisting of substances which, under normal conditions of temperature and pressure, exist as liquids or gases. This fraction is largely water, but it may contain appreciable quantities of carbon dioxide, sulfur dioxide and trioxide, chlorine, fluorine, nitrogen, argon, and other gases. When magma erupts at the surface of the earth, the gases are no longer confined within walls of rock and so tend to escape. Hence they are known as the **volatile substances** or **fugitive constituents.** It is only when lava chills rapidly to form a glass that large amounts of gases are retained. For this reason obsidian and other glassy rocks contain a much higher percentage of water and are chemically closer to magma than the crystalline rocks of otherwise similar compositions. In some pitchstones the water content may reach ten per cent. Pumice is a glassy rock, distended to a froth by rising bubbles of escaping gas. It gives a fair picture of the relative *volume* of gas under surface conditions.

As long as magma remains below the earth's surface, the imprisoned gases exert a strong outward pressure* that is more or less proportional to temperature. The magnitude of this pressure is demonstrated by the violence of explosive volcanic eruptions. Nearly all the volatile substances are lost during the course of normal crystallization in both intrusive and extrusive bodies. Except for small quantities that enter the composition of certain minerals (micas, amphiboles, etc.), the gaseous substances are rejected during crystallization. However, an even smaller fraction may be mechanically trapped as bubblelike inclusions.

The viscosity of magmas and lavas can be described only in terms

* In general, the solubilities of solids dissolved in liquids increase with higher temperatures, whereas the solubility of gases in liquids decreases as the temperature rises. Familiar examples are provided by air bubbles being "driven out" as water is heated and by the relative reluctance of iced tea to dissolve sugar.

of the effects that are produced. Viscous lava tends to pile up in doughlike masses that flow sluggishly as though they were being pushed. Extremely fluid lavas have been observed to move across flat country at rates of several miles per hour. Many solidified rocks display evidence of the physical behavior of the fluids that produced them, but the interpretation of the evidence yields only qualitative data. For instance, the parallel orientation of prismatic and platy crystals into lines of planes shows the direction of movement but does not indicate either the rate of flow or the fluidity. Similar evidence, equally difficult to evaluate, is given by the apparent movement of xenoliths. Some sills and other sheetlike masses are progressively richer in heavy minerals toward their lower contacts. This indicates that after these minerals had crystallized the magma was still sufficiently fluid to permit them to sink. Less often a zone of minerals of low specific gravity occurs near the upper contact, signifying that they have been buoyed upward by the greater density of the magma. In many localities even microscopic cavities in the wall rock have been invaded by fluids, and both wall rock and xenoliths may be soaked by mineral-bearing solutions. The penetration is so intimate that it seems to reflect the work of extremely mobile material, of vapors or thin liquids escaping from the intrusion, rather than invasion by the magma itself. This assumption is supported by the presence of minerals such as tourmaline that are characteristic of veins and pegmatites and relatively uncommon as primary constituents of igneous rocks.

The factors that control viscosity are temperature, chemical composition, gas content, and the amount of contained solids. Fluidity is increased by high temperature (the viscosity of water at the boiling point is a fraction of the value at room temperature) and by the presence of iron and volatiles. Conversely, lower temperatures, low gas content, and a large percentage of silica render magmas and lavas relatively viscous. In general, basaltic lavas tend to flow readily, whereas the rhyolites are pasty. The stage in magmatic history at which solids begin to appear is not known; nevertheless even the most rapidly congealed obsidians are packed with crystallites. Also many phaneric rocks contain flow lines and flow bands made up of early formed minerals oriented by movement. From these observa-

90

tions it seems clear that many, if not most, lavas and magmas change from liquid to a two-component system consisting of a liquid with suspended solids, long before they come to rest. The crystallites, crystals, and other solid inclusions cannot fail to affect the fluidity of the mixture. In addition to retarding flow, high viscosity impedes the escape of volatiles and slows the rate of crystallization.

The temperature of lava has been determined within several volcanic vents by direct but approximate measurements, but the temperature of magma within the earth can only be estimated by indirect methods. These include the effects of magma upon its surroundings, particularly the extent to which the minerals in wall rock or xenoliths have been altered or, in rare instances, melted. Further information is provided by the laboratory investigations of the temperatures at which minerals crystallize from artificial mixtures and by the determinations of the inversion temperatures of various minerals. The temperature of erupting lava appears to be on the order of 1000° C (corresponding to a bright red heat), but the surface may be even hotter as a result of the rapid oxidation of escaping gas. Knowledge of the temperatures of magma below the surface is even less definite, but most of the crystallization of intrusive rocks is believed to take place well below 1000° C.

Because the rock-forming minerals are polar compounds, it must be presumed that magma is an electrolyte and that its constituents are present as ions. Even though the make-up of the ions and the degree of ionization are not known, it is essential to bear in mind that magma is neither a mixture of the oxides used to report chemical analyses nor a mixture of melted minerals.

CRYSTALLIZATION

Solutions

When crystals begin to form in a liquid in which their ingredients were dissolved, they do so because they are no longer soluble under the prevailing conditions. Precipitation may proceed from several different causes, but the crystallization of minerals in magma and lava results primarily from cooling; temperature and temperature changes are the paramount factors in the solidification of igneous

91

rocks. A solution that contains the maximum amount of a dissolved substance is **saturated,** but it is saturated *only for the particular temperature concerned.* If the temperature is raised, the solvent is capable of accommodating a larger quantity of the solute, and the solution is accordingly **unsaturated.** If, on the other hand, the temperature of a saturated solution is lowered, two possibilities are open. Crystals of the solute may appear immediately. This may happen if crystals of the solid are already present or if the solution is agitated. However, if the temperature falls slowly, if the liquid is more or less at rest, and if it is not contaminated by crystals of the solute, the solution may be **supersaturated.** This means that the solution now contains more of the solute than would be present in a saturated solution.* Supersaturation is an unstable condition. Crystallization ensues when the supersaturation reaches a maximum or if the solution is either disturbed by movement or **inoculated** with crystals of the solute. Once crystals begin to appear, they continue to form until the solution is saturated. At this stage crystallization ceases until further cooling takes place. If the temperature were to rise, the solution would become unsaturated and tend to dissolve enough of the solid to bring it to saturation.

Texture

The cooling history is the most important factor in determining texture. When temperature falls rapidly, crystallization is correspondingly rapid, but the minerals are unable to attain large sizes, because crystallization begins at many closely spaced centers and the growing crystals mutually interfere. This accounts for the aphanitic texture of lava flows and small intrusions. With slow rates of cooling, crystallization starts at fewer, more widely separated points, and the slow rate of growth allows enough time for the minerals to attain the grain sizes characteristic of the phaneric rocks. Porphyritic rocks contain two or more generations of crystals. In most of these rocks, the phenocrysts are products of an early crystallization

---

* Water displays a phenomenon that is roughly analogous. If it is cooled slowly, the temperature may be lowered several degrees below O°C before ice is formed. Water in this state is said to be *supercooled.*

that proceeded slowly, and the aphanitic matrix represents a later and quicker cooling. The phenocrysts found in lava flows develop before the magma erupts at the surface.

Mineral growth is accomplished by the addition of ions to the surfaces of crystals. This necessitates the migration of ions through the solution, a process that takes place by **diffusion.** Diffusion is the tendency of ions or molecules to reach a uniform distribution throughout the medium. During the growth of a mineral, the ions

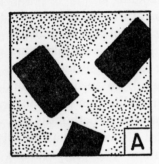 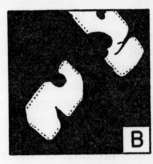

FIGURE 12.   **A,** schematic diagram of growing crystals (black) surrounded by zone from which the ions (dots) have been abstracted from the liquid. **B,** partially resorbed crystals of potash feldspar in obsidian.

in the immediate vicinity are attached to the crystal and thus reduce the concentration of ions in this zone (Figure 12A). Thus the rate at which crystals grow is dependent upon the rate at which diffusion supplies ions to the region that is being depleted. However, if the solution is in motion or is agitated by currents, diffusion may be aided by the stirring and mixing. High viscosity retards diffusion, and therefore crystallization takes place more freely in solutions that are relatively fluid. Obsidian, pitchstone, and similar rocks owe their glassy textures to the viscosity of their lavas. The rapid cooling of an already pasty lava increases viscosity to a point where the active diffusion of ions ceases. Glassy rocks are true solutions, viscous to a degree that makes them hard and brittle. Except for an occasional thin outer margin of glass, most basaltic flows are crystalline because of the relatively high mobility of basaltic lava. Glasses are unstable rocks, supersaturated with constituents that would have

93

crystallized under conditions more favorable for the development of minerals.

Cooling

Magmas cool partly by radiation, possibly through the escape of fluids, but largely by conduction. That cooling proceeds from the outside, inward, is clearly shown by zones of fine texture at igneous contacts and by the glassy margins of lava flows. Two factors significant in determining the rate of cooling are the mass and shape of the igneous body. If initial temperature and depth of burial are equal, a large mass will take longer to cool than a smaller one, as the total amount of heat to be lost is greater. Also dikes and sills cool faster than intrusions with smaller ratios of surface area to volume. Rock is excellent insulating material, an inefficient conductor of heat, and hence the cooling and crystallization of intrusives are extremely slow processes. From his studies of batholiths in California, Professor Esper Larsen of Harvard University has calculated the time required for their crystallization. The computations indicate intervals varying from a few hundred thousand to over a million years, depending upon the dimensions and depth. Such is the order of magnitude.

Crystallization is an **exothermic** process, which means that it is attended by the liberation of heat. When a gram of water turns to ice, eighty calories are set free. Similarly, the liquefaction of crystals is an **endothermic** process—heat is absorbed. To melt a gram of ice calls for the expenditure of eighty calories. Stated in other words, the **latent heat of fusion** of ice is 80 cal/g. Values for the latent heat of those minerals for which this property has been determined are of the same order. When minerals crystallize or when any other exothermic process contributes available heat, cooling and consequently crystallization are delayed. Conversely, endothermic changes hasten cooling.

Pressure

All ordinary crystalline substances, with the notable exception of ice, have higher densities than the same material in liquid form; a given mass of solid occupies a smaller volume than an equal mass of its liquid. Table 10 illustrates this difference by comparing the densities of certain minerals with glasses artificially prepared from them. Pressure facilitates crystallization, as it promotes changes that are attended by diminution of volume. Hence, under high pressure minerals may crystallize at higher temperatures than would be possible under less pressure.

TABLE 10. Comparison Between the Densities of Crystalline Materials and Glasses of the Same Composition

| | Specific Gravity | |
	Crystalline	Glass
Anorthite	2.765	2.700
Albite	2.605	2.382
Augite	3.266	2.835
Hornblende	3.216	2.826
Olivine	3.381	2.831
Orthoclase	2.551	2.351
Quartz	2.651	2.203
Diorite	2.880	2.710
Gabbro	2.940	2.791
Granite	2.656	2.446
Syenite	2.724	2.560

Note: Data from the *Handbook of Physical Constants*, Special Paper No. 36 of the Geological Society of America.

In many rhyolitic rocks, phenocrysts of quartz or feldspar indicate that their crystallization was followed by a partial dissolving. This process is known as **resorption.** The evidence is plainly seen in the rounded edges and corners of otherwise euhedral crystals and in the presence of smooth embayments (Fig. 12B). It may result from increase in temperature, brought about by the rapid oxidation of escaping volatiles, or be caused, in part, by a sudden drop of pressure accompanying extrusion. To what extent resorption may operate is not known; the completion of the process destroys the evidence.

SEPARATION OF MINERALS

When a mineral separates from solution, a state of equilibrium exists between the crystal and the liquid. Under the conditions that prevail, the mineral is stable and will be neither altered nor destroyed. However, as the magma continues to crystallize, changes are introduced. Temperature decreases, other minerals are formed, and the liquid becomes progressively richer in the substances that have not yet solidified or escaped. By these new conditions, the minerals formed earlier may or may not be affected. They may be partially or wholly dissolved (resorbed) or they may react with the liquid to such an extent that their early form and composition are radically changed. The adjustments that take place proceed always toward the establishment of equilibrium.

Many minerals have been produced in the laboratory from artificial melts. From these experiments, investigators have determined their **freezing points,** the temperatures at which they crystallize from the molten state. In nature, however, the crystallization of igneous minerals takes place in complex solutions of many constituents, and seldom, if ever, in a relatively pure melt. A mineral precipitates when the magma or lava reaches a stage at which the substance can no longer be held in solution. Consequently, minerals do not form at the temperatures indicated by their freezing points. For instance, magnesian olivine, Mg_2SiO_4, crystallizes from a pure melt of the same composition at 1890°C. The available evidence indicates that the temperatures of magmas are considerably lower than this and also that most minerals form at temperatures well below their freezing points. The order of crystallization is not fixed, as it would be if it followed the sequence of descending freezing points. The actual order in which minerals appear may vary; it depends upon solubility, which is controlled by other factors in addition to temperature.

The experimental investigation of igneous mixtures is an extremely difficult task. Few of the relationships between minerals are as simple as the two-component eutectic described in the following section. The magma is a multicomponent system, and many minerals are subject to modification after they have crystallized. High pressure and volatiles further complicate the study. In spite of the many handicaps, information is accumulating rapidly. For much of the specific, quantitative data, petrology is especially indebted to the Geophysical Laboratory and to Dr. N. L. Bowen and his colleagues at that institution. Their contributions are drawn upon extensively in these pages.

Eutectics

The crystallization temperatures of many substances are lowered by the presence of certain others in the same solution. The relationship is a mutual one; each substance lowers the crystallization point

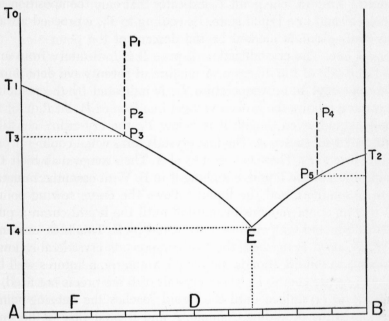

FIGURE 13.   Temperature-composition diagram of a hypothetical eutectic pair. For explanation see text.

of the other. The degree to which temperatures are affected is determined experimentally by observing the temperatures at which crystallization takes within artificial melts. These are made from many mixtures of varied proportions. A **temperature-composition** diagram (Figure 13) affords the simplest method for illustrating the principle. In these graphs, composition is plotted on the horizontal axis. Thus points A and B refer to compositions of pure A and pure B, respectively. A mixture of equal parts of A and B is indicated by point D, and point F represents a mixture consisting of eighty-

97

five per cent A and fifteen per cent B. The removal of either constituent will leave the remainder richer in the other. It is shown by moving the point in the appropriate direction. Temperatures are plotted on the vertical axis. Thus any combination of composition and temperature can be indicated by a point within the diagram. The curve, T_1ET_2, connects the points at which crystallization occurs from all possible mixtures. At all points above the curve, the material is liquid. The point T_0 indicates that only the A component is present and in a liquid state. Its cooling to T_1, where crystallization takes place, is marked by the descent of the point along the vertical line. The crystallization of pure B is indicated similarly at the right side of the diagram. A mixture of seventy per cent A and thirty per cent B, at temperature T_0, is indicated by the point P_1. Its cooling follows the broken vertical line toward P_3. At P_2 it is still wholly liquid, even though it is below T_1, the crystallization temperature of substance A. The first crystals form when cooling brings the mixture to P_3. These are crystals of A. Their removal changes the composition of the liquid, enriching it in B. With continued cooling more A solidifies, and the liquid follows the curve toward E. All the B component remains in solution until the liquid comes to the composition and temperature represented by E. This is the **eutectic point.** When it is reached, the two components crystallize simultaneously and solidification is completed. Similarly, a liquid shown by point P_4 would cool to P_5 where crystals of B are precipitated. They continue to crystallize until the liquid reaches the eutectic point. Here, as in the preceding example, A and B crystallize in the fixed proportion shown on the diagram. For any eutectic pair the eutectic point is unique—it fixes both the temperature and composition.

Crystallization temperatures are still further reduced when a third constituent (C) forms eutectic mixtures with the components of a eutectic pair. This gives rise to four eutectics: one between A and B, a second with A and C, another with B and C, and a fourth, a triple eutectic point involving all three constituents and with a temperature lower than those of the eutectic pairs. A hypothetical example is shown in Appendix C with the explanation of triangular composition diagrams.

Petrogenesis of the Igneous Rocks

In the formation of igneous rocks, eutectic relationships are important in lowering the temperatures at which the participating components crystallize from magma. The phenocrysts in certain porphyritic rocks have been explained by some petrologists as material in excess of an inferred eutectic complex represented by the matrix.

Plagioclase Feldspar

Between the albite and anorthite end members, plagioclase includes a complete, uninterrupted series of isomorphous compounds. The crystallization of the system, established by N. L. Bowen in 1913, provides a key to the understanding of other isomorphous groups of minerals. The freezing points of anorthite and albite, from pure melts of these substances, are 1550°C and 1100°C, respectively. When an intermediate plagioclase crystallizes under favorable conditions and the temperature continues to fall, it tends to react with the surrounding liquid. As a result, the crystal acquires a new composition, slightly richer in albite. The change continues progressively, without breaks, until solidification is complete. For this reason, plagioclase and other minerals that follow a similar pattern are described as **continuous reaction series.**

The course of crystallization can be traced on the temperature-composition diagram, reproduced as Figure 14. On this chart, any mixture represented by a point above the upper curve (the **liquidus**) is liquid, and similarly, points below the lower curve (the **solidus**) indicate crystalline material. If a hypothetical liquid, of composition and temperature shown by point A, is cooled, the first crystals will appear when the falling temperature brings the mixture to B on the liquidus. These crystals have the composition indicated by point C, *they are the only crystals that can exist in equilibrium with the liquid shown by B.* Since these crystals are richer in the anorthite end member, their removal leaves the liquid richer in albite. With continued cooling and further crystallization, the changes in the liquid cause it to follow the downward slope of the liquidus. The crystals of composition C are then no longer in equilibrium with the liquid. If the cooling is slow enough to permit, a reaction ensues

99

which changes the crystals to a composition that is stable in the presence of the liquid. This composition is the same as that of the crystals currently precipitating.

At any stage in the process, a horizontal line projected from a point on the liquidus to the solidus indicates the composition of the

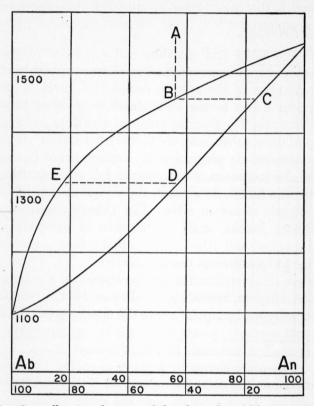

FIGURE 14.   Crystallization diagram of the plagioclase feldspars. After Bowen. For explanation see text.

crystals being formed from this liquid. It is also the composition to which the earlier crystals are being made over. Both the newly formed crystals and those being modified become progressively richer in albite. Thus the crystalline phase follows the solidus toward D. If the process goes to completion without interference from other factors, the completely solidified feldspar will all have the composi-

100

tion indicated by D, with the same Ab/An ratio as the original liquid. The last trace of liquid is represented by E.

When rapid crystallization prevents these reactions from taking place, each plagioclase crystal consists of a homogeneous core surrounded by layers of different compositions. The center is the first to form, and is therefore richer in anorthite than the liquid from which it precipitated. Each successive layer contains a higher albite

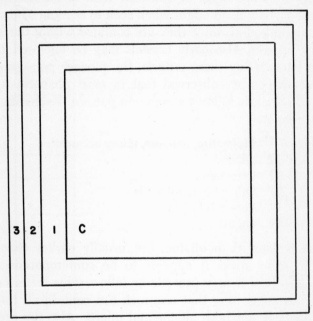

FIGURE 15. Schematic section through a zoned crystal. Each of the successive layers 1, 2, and 3 has a volume equal to that of the cubic core C.

content than the one below, and the outer layers are richer in this end member than the original liquid. Also each layer seals the one below from contact with the liquid. The **zoned** structure that results is particularly common in the feldspars of diorites and related rocks. It occurs also in pyroxenes and other minerals. Zoning, however, is seldom visible in hand specimens, but can be seen occasionally in coarse feldspar phenocrysts. In estimating the relative volumes of core and successive additions it is necessary to take into account the third dimension that is not seen in a cross section (Figure 15).

101

Order of Crystallization

Because a mineral precipitates when the cooling magma attains the necessary supersaturation, this factor fixes the order in which the different minerals shall appear. Minerals that form during the early stages when the ratio of solid to liquid is small have ample room to develop euhedral crystals. Phenocrysts provide the best examples. In the intermediate stages the minerals tend to be subhedral, exhibiting one or two clean edges when seen in section. Minerals that form late are anhedral, since they are confined within the irregular spaces that remain. Also early crystals may be enclosed by those that come later. Using these criteria, the pioneer petrographers of the nineteenth century observed that in *most* phaneric rocks the sequence of minerals follows a common pattern. Excluding plagioclase, the order is:

I   Magnetite, ilmenite, minor accessories
II   Olivine
III   Pyroxene
IV   Other femic minerals
V   Potash feldspar
VI   Quartz

Plagioclase is later than olivine, but usually earlier than potash feldspar. In some rocks it appears to be contemporaneous with pyroxene, in others it may precede or follow. This list is not to be interpreted as suggesting that one rock can contain all these minerals, particularly not both olivine and quartz. Also the crystallization of the minerals overlaps; the appearance of one is not delayed until the crystallization of its predecessor is complete. Furthermore, exceptions to this sequence are both conspicuous and common, as, for instance, phenocrysts of quartz and potash feldspar.

Laboratory experiments with artificial compounds have been successful in reproducing part of the sequence commonly observed in rocks. Although technical difficulties limit these studies to relatively simple minerals, the investigators have assembled enough data to formulate certain definite principles. Evidence, visible with the microscope, invites the extension of these principles to the crystallization of the more complex minerals such as biotite and the amphiboles. Among the many laboratory investigations, one (by Bowen and Anderson) affords a particularly valuable illustration of a pattern frequently involved in the separation of femic minerals. A brief summary follows.

Silica and magnesia are mixed in the proportions represented by the formula $MgSiO_3$ (magnesian pyroxene, enstatite). The mixture is fused and then *slowly* cooled. The first crystals to precipitate have the composition of olivine (Mg_2SiO_4). This compound has a higher magnesia content than the original material. As it continues to separate, the liquid is correspondingly enriched in silica. The crystallization of olivine ceases at a point determined by the composition of the liquid and the temperature. When it is reached, pyroxene crystallizes directly from solution, and the liquid begins to react with the olivine, converting it to pyroxene. If sufficient time is allowed, the conversion is complete and the final solid consists entirely of pyroxene. If the original mixture is prepared with a composition intermediate between olivine and pyroxene, the results will be similar. More olivine forms than is indicated by the mix, but with slow cooling the excess will be converted to pyroxene by reaction with the liquid. The completely solidified product will consist of pyroxene and olivine in the proportions with which the experiment started.

A point to be emphasized is that the reaction between solid and liquid changes one mineral (olivine) directly to another (pyroxene), with entirely different physical characteristics. There are no intermediate stages. Minerals exhibiting this relationship are described as **reaction pairs,** and the conversion of one to another as a **discontinuous reaction.** The terminology is useful in keeping clear the distinction between the foregoing and the continuous reaction through a series of isomorphous compounds exemplified by plagioclase. It will be noted also that a liquid with the composition of pyroxene may become supersaturated with olivine and precipitate olivine before the conditions require the separation of pyroxene. From this it seems possible for a magma to produce minerals at one stage that may be destroyed during another, so that no trace of them appears in the solid rock.

The reactions within actual magmas necessarily involve many more constituents and more complex products than those dealt with in the laboratory. The pyroxenes comprise a group of particularly diverse compositions. Chemical analyses of some require the determination of nine oxides. Even though the intimate details of their crystallization have yet to be learned, something of their history can be interpreted from their relationships as seen with the microscope. In many rocks the pyroxenes are distinctly zoned and thereby indicate that changes of composition were in progress during crystallization. The evidence is also clear that pyroxene is often converted to amphibole. Minerals with the outward form of pyroxene, but with the composition and other properties of amphibole, are by no means uncommon. Also many hornblendes contain an inner core of pyroxene, or small individual hornblende crystals may form a mantle, a **reaction rim**, enclosing a larger crystal of pyroxene. Even though experimental confirmation is lacking, it is difficult to escape the conclusion that pyroxene and hornblende constitute a reaction pair. Biotite occurs in the same relationship to hornblende as that described between hornblende and pyroxene. Occasionally these minerals are seen in concentric arrangement; a center of pyroxene is enclosed within hornblende, which, in turn, is surrounded by biotite. Thus the sequence olivine-pyroxene-hornblende-biotite constitutes a discontinuous reaction series, in which each two adjacent minerals are members of a reaction pair.

ROCK GENESIS

The Gabbro-Granite Sequence

Every igneous rock type represents an assemblage of minerals, but the number of rocks that actually occur is only a small fraction of the combinations of minerals that are mathematically possible. A major problem of petrogenesis is to explain how minerals are brought together to form these particular combinations.

In the familiar rocks of the larger intrusions, the granites, granodiorites, diorites, and gabbros, the development of minerals nearly always follows the pattern indicated in Table 11. Exceptions are numerous, but the order is sufficiently common to serve as a general guide to the crystallization of batholiths and large intrusive sheets. At the upper left, the femic minerals are arranged in the order of appearance, and their linkage as successive reaction pairs is suggested by the broken connecting lines. The continuous reaction series of plagioclase is shown at the right. Within this series the order is one of decreasing lime and increasing soda, but the position of any particular plagioclase is not fixed with respect to the femic minerals in the opposite column. Potash feldspar, muscovite, and

TABLE 11. Order of Crystallization

Note: From N. L. Bowen, modified.

quartz crystallize during a late stage; they consist of substances either not demanded by the earlier minerals or present in excess of the required amounts. The early minerals are characterized by low silica and absence of water. Consequently the magma is progressively enriched in these constituents, and they enter increasingly into the products of later crystallization.

If the arrangement of minerals is considered horizontally rather than vertically, it will be seen that the distribution falls naturally into the various associations that define the major igneous rock types. A hypothetical magma will first precipitate olivine followed by pyroxene and calcic plagioclase. These are the minerals of gabbro;

105

the crystallization is that of the gabbroic stage. When hornblende and intermediate plagioclase begin to appear, they are formed in part directly from the magma and in part by reaction between the magma and the earlier crystals. The crystallization has entered the dioritic stage, and the olivine will have disappeared. Similarly, the granodiorite stage begins with appearance of potash feldspar and passes into the granite stage when orthoclase or microcline becomes the predominate feldspar. There is no firm basis for presuming that every magma that has produced a granite shall have passed through all these stages. However, the *order* of events is clearly attested in many rocks by the evidence of zoned crystals, reaction rims, and pseudomorphs after earlier minerals.

Residual Fluids

Because the magma contains water and other volatile substances beyond the capacity of the "normal" igneous rock minerals to use them, they are rejected during the course of crystallization. To what extent they reduce the viscosity of magma and lower crystallization temperatures is not yet known, and whether they act as catalysts in promoting mineral formation is even more problematical. Whatever their role may be during crystallization, the visible effects of the volatiles are not produced until the latest stage of magmatic history. Unless these substances have escaped earlier, the final fluid part of a magma consists of the volatiles and the last fraction of the magma. The chief ingredients are therefore water and silica, with the other components of alkali feldspar and mica. In addition, there may be appreciable quantites of many elements that do not enter the composition of the igneous minerals. It is noteworthy that the various phenomena attributed to such fluids are commonly associated with granites and closely related rocks and that they are sometimes found with the alkalic rocks, but are seldom conspicuous in gabbro. For these reasons, the effects produced by **end stage fluids** can be regarded as continuing the crystallization history of the magma. Although there are insufficient data to describe the physical state of the end stage fluids, their extremely low viscosity is demonstrated by their intimate penetration of host rock, xenoliths, and wall rock, and their exploration of cleavage planes and other directions of weakness. In lava, a high silica content results in high viscosity; the end stage fluids are silicious, but their mobility is accounted for by the preponderance of water. Whether or not they are correctly designated as **aqueous solutions,** water appears to be the medium by which the other substances are conveyed.

During the late stages of crystallization, the residual fluid is confined within constantly narrowing limits, as more and more of the available space is occupied by minerals precipitated directly from the magma. When a way is opened along joints or some other weakness in the host, the residual fluids concentrate in these places, following them to escape into the wall rock, or as far as they persist, and filling them with minerals. When these solutions explore a more or less plane fracture, the subsequent fillings are classified as pegmatite dikes, aplite dikes, or quartz veins, depending upon the material precipitated. A space of irregular shape will give rise to a correspondingly formless mass of these substances. When these solutions are trapped within the parent rock and held in a disseminated condition, they may form veinlets invisible to the naked eye, but their principal effect is to react with the igneous minerals and convert them to new products. This process, termed **deuteric alteration,** is described in Chapter 7.

Pegmatite

In the pegmatites associated with granite, the most conspicuous minerals are quartz, orthoclase, microcline, sodic plagioclase, muscovite, and biotite. Among the many other minerals that may be present, a large number are particularly characteristic of pegmatite, although they are not necessarily restricted to this origin. Pegmatites also contain elements and minerals that are comparatively rare in other rocks; where these substances are sufficiently concentrated the pegmatite becomes an important commercial deposit. Among the minerals obtained from this source are feldspar, mica, beryl, and nearly all the gems except the diamond. The list of pegmatite minerals in Table 12 includes those that are most abundant and a few familiar minerals that are either typical or economically important.

Coarse texture is the outstanding physical characteristic of pegmatite bodies; crystals over forty feet long have been recorded, and minerals several inches in diameter are common. However, the texture is seldom uniform, and excessively large crystals may occur adjacent to those of smaller and different sizes. Intergrowths of quartz and feldspar that have developed in a geometrically regular pattern are known as **graphic granite** (Figure 16). This structure occurs frequently. Throughout the host which is nearly always microcline,

TABLE 12. Minerals in Pegmatite

	Remarks
Quartz	rose quartz
Orthoclase	
Microcline	
Sodic plagioclase	common and abundant
Muscovite	
Biotite	
Garnet	
Apatite	chlorine, fluorine
Corundum	includes ruby, sapphire
Beryl	beryllium, emerald, aquamarine
Tourmaline	boron, semi-precious stones
Rubellite (lithia tourmaline)	boron, lithium
Lepidolite (lithia mica)	lithium
Spodumene (lithia pyroxene)	lithium
Topaz	fluorine, gems
Fluorite	fluorine
Cryolite	fluorine, aluminum **ore**
Chrysoberyl	beryllium, gems
Cassiterite	tin ore
Molybdenite	molybdenum ore
Wolframite	tungsten ore
Arsenopyrite	arsenic
Uraninite (pitchblende)	uranium, radium, ore

the quartz is uniformly distributed. The individual patches of quartz that are seen on a broken surface have similar shapes and sizes and are arranged in a parallel pattern. Also, although they are not connected, their crystallographic elements are mutually parallel. It is as though the separate units of quartz were all part of a single crystal. When graphic granite is analyzed mechanically, it is found to consist nearly always of 74 parts of feldspar with 26 parts of quartz. By some investigators it is interpreted as the simultaneous crystallization of its two components as a eutectic mixture. Others consider that the feldspar forms first, and that the quartz enters later by selective replacement.

Dikelike bodies of pegmatite may invade the parent intrusive or be found in the wall rock. Their trend may follow fractures or foliation,

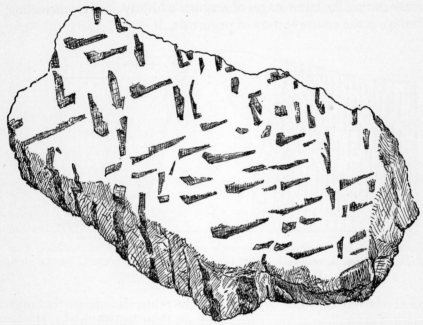

FIGURE 16.   Graphic granite. Quartz (wedge-shaped inclusions) distributed in parallel alignment through a microcline crystal. Drawn by Paul Dobbs.

or else cut across the structural features. Irregularly shaped masses sometimes occur at the contact, forming a caplike body between the intrusive and the country rock. In some pegmatites no particular structure is apparent. Others are distinctly banded, often with one set of minerals arranged in a certain texture at the contact with the walls and a second set separating this layer from the material that occupies the center of the mass (Figure 17). When it is possible to trace pegmatite into its parent intrusion, it appears to merge gradually into its source; the typical pegmatite minerals disappear, and the crystals acquire the texture of the main rock. There are no "roots."

With a few exceptions, petrologists in general agree that pegmatites are precipitated from residual fluids rich in water and other volatiles and also in silica. The evidence set forth for this origin is the close field association with intrusions, and the correspondence between pegmatite minerals and those formed within some igneous rocks during the latest stages of magmatic history. The extraordinary feature is the coarse texture of pegmatite. It cannot be explained by

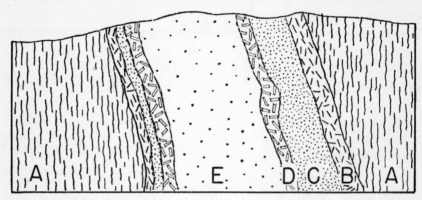

FIGURE 17. Section through a strongly zoned pegmatite dike, modified from E. N. Cameron. **A,** wall rock. **B,** quartz, plagioclase, mica zone. **C,** biotite zone. **D,** muscovite-rich zone. **E,** quartz core.

an excessively slow rate of cooling, as the minerals indicate that pegmatites crystallize at lower temperatures than igneous rocks. Hence it is difficult to avoid the conclusion that the minerals, in spite of their large size, form within a relatively short time. One explanation, not entirely convincing, is that crystallization proceeds rapidly in the presence of large quantities of water and that some of the other volatiles act as catalysts to the same effect.

The minerals within a pegmatite are not necessarily limited to a single stage of crystallization. Separate zones, with contacts approximately parallel to the walls, indicate a distinct order of deposition, from the contacts inward (Figure 17). Furthermore, evidence from many localities has been presented to show that residual fluids are subject to changes in composition. The earlier generation may consist of a barren mixture of quartz and feldspar, later replaced by minerals rich in volatiles.

Aplite

In its association with granite and closely related rocks, aplite is similar to pegmatite. It occurs commonly as dikes perpendicular to flow structures and as irregular masses at the contact of intrusions. The minerals are orthoclase or microcline, quartz, and muscovite, but it may carry relatively small quantities of biotite and other minerals. Typical aplite consists of equidimensional crystals, less than two millimeters in diameter. This feature, together with its equigranular habit, gives the rock a strikingly saccharoidal (sugary) appearance, an effect that is heightened by the preponderance of light-colored minerals. Aplite, like pegmatite, is formed by the crystallization of residual fluid; the two rocks appear to have a common time and place of origin and presumably form at about the same temperature. Also they may occur together, associated with the same granite intrusion. The difference in texture is extreme. Aplite is fine and remarkably uniform; pegmatite is coarse and varied. The difference is attributed to the relative abundance of volatiles in the residual fluid. If the volatile fraction separates from a fluid which otherwise would form pegmatite, the remainder is left as a highly silicious and therefore highly viscous liquid. The viscosity of this aplite magma leads to the production of fine crystals. This hypothesis requires openings for the escape of the volatile substances. One possibility lies in fractures produced by the shrinkage that invariably attends cooling.

Quartz Veins

Many igneous rocks contain segregations of quartz, as veins, lenses, or in formless patches. The characteristic varieties are milky quartz, and a gray, semi-translucent material. It is devoid of crystal forms and intimately and irregularly fractured. The manner of deposition is uncertain. Except in the presence of alkalies, the solubility of quartz is extremely low, and its transportation would therefore require disproportionately large quantities of water. As an alternative, it has been frequently asserted that quartz is carried and deposited as colloidal particles. The colloidal silica then congeals to a gel and subsequently crystallizes.

FEMIC ROCKS AND ANORTHOSITE

Gravity Separation of Minerals

When gabbro magma begins to crystallize, olivine is the first silicate mineral to appear. It is followed by pyroxene and plagioclase. These minerals may form simultaneously, or one may precede the other. The specific gravities of both olivine and pyroxene are appreciably higher than that of the rock considered as a unit and considerably higher than the density of the liquid that remains after they have crystallized. That this density difference may lead to the sinking of the early, iron-magnesia minerals is attested in many sheetlike intrusions. Sometimes it is manifested by a concentration of heavy minerals in a zone near the lower contact, with a corresponding increase in the abundance of lighter minerals at higher levels. Density stratification of this kind may produce several zones, and the process is effective in varying degrees. It may fail to operate altogether, or it may be so slight as to have no obvious effect on the apparent homogeneity of the rock. Under these circumstances it may be revealed only by a careful mechanical analysis of samples from different levels. In its extreme form, density stratification produces entirely different rocks, each confined to a distinct layer and separated above and below by a sharp, nontransitional contact. In this way, crystals sinking in a gabbro magma may produce a concentration of olivine crystals (dunite), a similar concentration of pyroxene (pyroxenite), or a mixture of olivine and pyroxene (peridotite, in a limited sense). Some ore bodies consisting of magnetite, titaniferous magnetite, or chromite are formed by a similar segregation of these heavy metallic minerals. The field association of some dunite, pyroxenite, and related peridotite, with gabbro, presents a clear case for their origin by crystal sorting.

The Palisades dolerite sill of New Jersey is a widely known and comparatively simple illustration of gravity sorting of crystals. This sill has been studied for more than half a century and has been reinvestigated recently by Dr. F. Walker. The following summary is taken from his detailed account. The sill has a probably maximum thickness of a thousand feet. Its abundant constituents are plagioclase, pyroxene, and olivine. At the upper and lower contacts the rock is aphanitic, and the chilled zone at the base has a composition closely approximating the average composition of the entire sill. Within these aphanitic zones the cooling was sufficiently rapid to produce the fine texture and prevent the downward movement of crystals. Olivine constitutes about one per cent of this part of the rock. At a level of from thirty to sixty feet above the base there is a persistent layer of variable thickness, the "olivine-rich zone," which may contain as much as twenty-five per cent olivine. Above this zone the olivine diminishes rapidly and disappears completely within a hundred feet of the lower contact. From the olivine zone upward the amount of pyroxene gradually decreases and plagioclase becomes correspondingly more abundant. The changes in texture and mineralogy in the lower part of the sill are shown diagrammatically in Figure 18. In the upper part of the sill, but not in the chilled zone, there is a small percentage of quartz, crystallized from residual fluid. Some of the quartz is concentrated in narrow veins of pegmatite.

The factors that control the rate of descent of solid particles through a liquid are the size and shape of the particles, the difference in density of solid and liquid, and the viscosity of the liquid. Effective gravity separation is therefore possible only when cooling and crystallization proceed slowly, so that the early minerals may reach a sufficient size to be affected, and so that their descent is not impeded either by the increasing viscosity of the liquid or by the interference of later crystals. This is illustrated by the arrest of the olivine crystals in the Palisades sill at a level above the base of the intrusion. The lowest zone, previously noted, consists of aphanitic rock. Its relatively rapid cooling, attested by both fine texture and homogeneity, prevented the penetration by the sinking olivine crystals. Quartz, which appears in the upper part of the intrusion, would not be expected in a homogeneous sill if the composition were uniform throughout. It is explained (p. 103) by the general tendency of olivine to crystallize in larger amounts than the absolute composition of the magma requires. In the absence of a mechanism for separating the solid from the liquid, excess olivine is subsequently converted to pyroxene. However, the removal of olivine leaves the liquid richer in silica, so that in the present illustration it has remained to form quartz.

113

The absence of sorting phenomena in igneous intrusions may result from either magma that is too viscous or from the failure of heavy minerals to crystallize in advance of the others. There is little

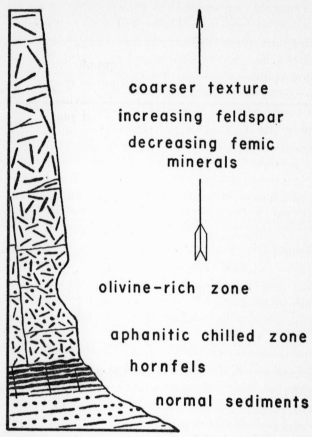

coarser texture

increasing feldspar

decreasing femic minerals

olivine-rich zone

aphanitic chilled zone

hornfels

normal sediments

FIGURE 18.   Section of the lower part of the Palisades sill of New Jersey. The steep face of the cliff is controlled by columnar joints. The notch near the base marks the edge of the olivine-rich zone. It results from the rapid weathering of olivine.

or no evidence of comparable density stratification in stocks and batholiths. Neither of these intrusions has a known floor, and no example is recorded of erosion having proceeded to a depth great enough to reveal more than their upper parts. Hence it is impossible to determine from field evidence whether the *batholithic* granites and similar rocks have undergone sorting by gravity. However, a gravity separation may occur within granites intruded as sheets. According to one general hypothesis, supported by many petrologists, nearly all magma is generated in a deep zone of either basalt or peridotite and so begins its ascent with one or the other of these compositions. Its upward journey is one of a score of miles, or more, and requires a long but indeterminate interval of time. Presumably it may allow sufficient opportunity for the crystallization and sinking of a large part of the femic material. Under this hypothesis, a granite batholith could be regarded as the uppermost portion of a deep igneous plug, the silicious fraction that remains after the withdrawal of compounds rich in iron and magnesia. Professor Daly has postulated a continuous shell of basaltic composition beginning at a depth of about twenty-five miles and conforming to the concentric structure of the earth that is known through the study of earthquake vibrations. This has been termed the **basaltic substratum.** The evidence for a common source of much basalt is given by the close chemical similarity of many basalts throughout the world, particularly of those extruded as fissure eruptions. If magma is guided upward along deep fractures, its rise may be too rapid to permit internal changes before it is extruded as a lava.

Anorthosite

Anorthosite is a coarse-textured rock consisting of plagioclase, usually labradorite, and little else. In most, but not all, localities it shows evidence of considerable crushing. It commonly occurs with other rocks, particularly gabbro, as part of a lopolith or sheet intrusion. No rocks of similar composition with an aphanitic, glassy, or other habit suggesting an effusive character have ever been discovered. Also a liquid of the same composition could exist only at temperatures above the range considered normal for magmas. For these two reasons petrologists agree that the feldspars have in some fashion been segregated from a magma of more "normal" composition. Two main hypotheses, with several minor variations, have been advanced to explain the peculiar mineral make-up of anorthosite. According to one, it develops during the crystallization of gabbroic magma; the femic minerals crystallize during an early stage and sink

115

to leave the upper liquid consisting of material for plagioclase alone. According to the other hypothesis, plagioclase crystallizes before most of the other minerals, forming in a magma variously regarded as representing gabbro, diorite, or granodiorite. The plagioclase crystals are lathlike in shape and are arranged at random to form an open meshwork or lattice. The space between the feldspar is occupied by the remaining liquid portion of the magma. If this mixture of solid crystals and interstitial liquid is then subjected to pressure, two results will follow. The liquid is pressed out of the framework of feldspar, as water is squeezed from a sponge, and is forced into the surrounding rock where it crystallizes as stringers and tongues. The feldspars are jammed together, partly broken and crushed, and so form a solid mass of anorthosite. Both hypotheses are supported by field evidence.

Assimilation and Syntexis

If a magma succeeds in incorporating rocks from its walls and roof, its composition will be changed in proportion to the amount and kind of foreign material that it assimilates. The process is termed **syntexis,** and the resulting product is a **syntectic** rock. That syntexis does occur is abundantly shown by the presence of xenoliths in various stages of digestion (Figure 8), but the extent to which syntexis is able to operate, its actual mechanism, and the kinds of rock that can be incorporated within magmas are still under investigation. Complete assimilation destroys the direct evidence of the process. Dr. Bowen has shown that both the melting and dissolving of solid rock by magma is sharply limited by the amount of heat that is available, as both of these processes are endothermic and lead to the rapid cooling of the magma. On the other hand, the crystallization of minerals within a magma is an exothermic change. Thus both the formation of new crystals and the exchanges involved in the substitutions of the continuous and discontinuous reactions (p. 103) result in the evolution of heat. From this he concludes that a magma, currently producing one set of minerals, may react with others introduced as xenoliths, provided that these are higher in the reaction series (p. 105) than the minerals being precipitated. Thus a magma, still sufficiently liquid and precipitating hornblende and andesine, would be able to react with pyroxene and labradorite, and convert them to hornblende and andesine. The magma, at the same stage, would not react with biotite or albite, as it would not be saturated with these minerals.

The role of volatiles in syntexis is far less clear. Water is a primary constituent of every magma, and its amount may be increased when rocks such as shale are engulfed. Carbon dioxide is added when xenoliths of carbonate rocks are heated to the point required for the dissociation of calcite and similar minerals. Water facilitates most inorganic chemical reactions and with the other volatile substances is important in determining the character of end stage fluids and their products. However, until the action of the volatiles shall have been further investigated and better understood, it will be impossible to evaluate their part in syntexis and their significance in producing rocks of mixed compositions.

Alkaline Rocks

Rocks rich in alkali feldspar, including those that contain the feldspathoid minerals, nepheline, leucite, sodalite, and analcite, have been explained by various hypotheses. Since many nepheline syenites are found in close association with larger bodies of granite and some show direct gradations to granite, most of the opinions concerning their origin have dealt with methods of deriving nepheline syenite from granite magma. Each major hypothesis set forth to this end has been subjected to searching analysis and vigorously debated. Typical among these is one presented by Professor R. A. Daly and supported especially by Professor S. J. Shand, but opposed by others. This hypothesis holds that nepheline syenite is formed, at most of the places where it occurs, through the assimilation of limestone. It contends that, at most localities where nepheline syenite appears, the magma has either come into contact with limestone or calcareous sediments or has risen through such formations. When limestone is assimilated by magma, lime silicates are formed, and these being heavier than the liquid, tend to sink. The process removes silica from the magma and adds a large quantity of carbon dioxide. The magma is thus enriched in alkalies, and the volatile fraction is reinforced by carbon dioxide and possibly by water

117

from the sediments. Sodium carbonate and sodium metasilicate (Na_2SiO_3) are formed. These compounds are highly soluble and are carried by the volatiles. Nepheline is produced by the reaction between sodium carbonate and albitic liquid, and the carbon dioxide escapes. The hypothesis finds support in the presense of minerals that include the carbonate radical (cancrinite) and others that contain water or other substances usually associated with the volatile constituents. The principal objection to the hypothesis is the large supply of heat necessary to dissociate calcite and dissolve the lime. In answering this objection, adherents of the hypothesis insist that only a small fraction of the magma so involved crystallizes as nepheline rock, often less than one per cent and that the effects are concentrated within this restricted part. In conclusion, it is to be emphasized that the petrologists who are particularly concerned with alkaline rocks are generally agreed that no single explanation serves to account for all the rocks in this most diversified group.

GRANITIZATION

In many regions, rocks that were formerly either sedimentary or metamorphic are represented by mixtures. The original material has been impregnated by mobile substances that have produced the minerals typical of granite. The products of such invasions are highly variable. Solutions, guided by foliation or bedding, may crystallize as definite thin sheets along the planes of weakness. The process is known as **lit-par-lit** intrusion and results in rocks with pronounced banded structures. When the bands occur in small and tightly crumpled complex folds, they are taken as evidence that the invaded rocks were in a plastic, or almost plastic, state when the intrusion took place. In some rocks the effects appear to be purely mechanical, with little or no alteration of the original minerals and structures. Elsewhere the minerals have been made over to compositions similar to those of the introduced minerals. Original structures may be almost wholly retained even when replacement has changed the composition. On the other hand, the bedding or foliation may be only faintly preserved by minor differences, either of color or of mineral orientation. Sometimes it is visible only on freshly exposed surfaces, or conversely, in places where weathering has served to accentuate inconspicuous differences. The invasion of a rock may be selective in that the transforming substances affect only certain lithologic units, leaving others unchanged and standing in strong contrast. On the other hand, they may penetrate a rock without regard to its composition or structural habit.

When schistose or slaty rocks are strongly altered, enough of their original parallelism may remain to give them the appearance of

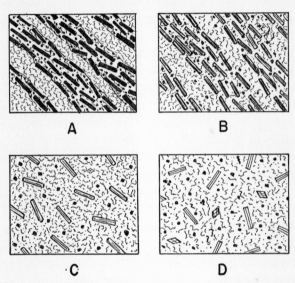

FIGURE 19. Granitization by fluid emanations. **A**, lit-par-lit intrusion; gneiss (black bars and dots) invaded along the foliation by solutions carrying quartz and feldspar (irregular broken lines). **B**, the metamorphic minerals have been transformed to other species, but their outlines and arrangement have been preserved. **C**, the rock is completely granitized, but the prismatic or platy minerals retain a subparallel arrangement. **D**, massive granitized rock with no visible evidence of inherited structure.

feldspathic and silicious gneisses. A more intense transformation produces rock resembling granite with a pronounced primary flow structure, and in an extreme form the alteration yields a rock indistinguishable from massive granite and with no visible evidence of parallel structure. In their field distribution these rocks may display similar gradations. One may pass from an obviously metamorphic schist or gneiss to a rock that is mildly invaded and affected, and

119

thence through mixed rocks of increasingly granitic composition to unmodified granite. The process of making over a solid rock to one with the textural habit and mineralogy of granite is termed **granitization.** (Figure 19).

Gneisses with mixed compositions, consisting of invaded and invading material, have been known for many years. However the study has recently been intensified by the claims of some adherents of granitization, who hold that practically all granites, including those of batholiths, have been transformed by replacement. Several aspects of the inquiry are:

1. The physical and chemical make-up of the transforming substances.
2. The criteria by which products of granitization are to be distinguished from granites of magmatic origin.
3. The extent to which granitization has operated, the relative quantities of granitized and igneous granite.

One absolute requirement for invading substances, is that they be sufficiently mobile to penetrate solid rock. This condition appears to be met by the volatile substances of magma, for these constituents give abundant evidence of their ability to penetrate and soak firm material in intimate fashion. Since these fluids are rich in silica and the ingredients of alkali feldspar and occur in quantity in granite magma, they provide a possible agent of granitization. According to a different hypothesis they may rise from some deep and unknown source, or they may proceed as a wave of transforming fluid in advance of a rising granite magma, or they may escape from granite following the emplacement and partial crystallization of a batholithic mass. The common close occurrence of mixed granite gneisses with presumably intrusive granite tends to support the hypothesis of granitization by emanations from granite magma. The localities that show this relationship are regarded as regions where erosion has cut deep and exposed structures that were formed far below the level of the present surface.

Another hypothesis assumes that granitization is caused by ions migrating upward without being transported by water or some other fluid medium. The ions move along the boundaries between crystals, through the empty spaces within crystalline structure, and from point to point within the crystal framework.

Petrogenesis of the Igneous Rocks

The criteria for the recognition of granite and granitized rock are not yet established. However, the preservation of inherited sedimentary and metamorphic structures in a rock of granitic composition would seem to be valid evidence of replacement. Similarly the existence of clean, sharp, nongradational boundaries, the presence of dikes and apophyses, especially if they are transgressive, and of fine-textured margins seem clear indications of a true igneous contact.

Conclusion

Igneous petrology, like every other division of scientific inquiry, is concerned with approaches toward the solution of a variety of unexplained and partly explained problems. It is the nature of science that each goal has a tendency to recede and split into other problems when the investigations have almost reached a conclusion. No answer can be final when it leads to other, frequently unsuspected, phenomena, that are no less elusive than the ones sought earlier. Some of the major, current problems of petrogenesis are listed below. Each concerns a process that is supported by evidence. The questions to which they give rise do not deal with their validity, but inquire about their mechanisms and the more difficult quantitative problem of the extent to which each one operates.

Genesis of magma
1. Erupted from a continuous femic source
2. By melting of deeply buried sedimentary and metamorphic rocks
3. Solid rock rendered mobile by the penetration of active heated fluids

Origin of granite
1. Crystallized from magma
2. Produced by granitization

Diversity of rocks
1. Crystal sorting by gravity and pressure
2. Assimilation of wall rock: Syntexis
3. Original differences of local primary magmas

SUGGESTIONS FOR STUDY

1. Compare specimens from the inner parts of dikes and sills with others from the contacts, for observable differences in texture and mineralogy.

2. Examine specimens that illustrate the following:
    a. Zoned crystals.
    b. Embayed and rounded phenocrysts.
    c. Pegmatite; graphic granite, coarse texture.
    d. Aplite.
    e. Anorthosite with cataclastic structure.
    f. Xenoliths.
    g. Reaction rims.
    h. Lit-par-lit intrusion.

.7.

Altered Rocks

In GENERAL, a rock is in complete equilibrium with its environment only when it is in the process of being assembled,* and is subject to alteration when changes take place in the temperature, pressure, or chemical provenance. The measure of change impressed upon a rock is determined by the difference between the conditions that prevailed when it was formed and those to which it was later exposed, and also by the stability of the rock in various surroundings. Hence the adjustments may be so slight as to escape observation, or they may destroy the original characteristics and lead to a complete reorganization of all the constituents.

Except for brecciation induced by simple mechanical stress from without, the alteration of rock involves both physical and chemical changes that are mutually dependent. The principal categories are: metamorphism, weathering, devitrification, hydrothermal alteration, and deuteric alteration. Metamorphic processes take place under the influence of increased pressure and temperature; on the whole, metamorphism is an integrating change tending to produce complex rather than simple substances. Metamorphism is considered in Chapter 9. The account on the following pages concerns the results of processes that break down and destroy rocks.

BRECCIA

Breccias are accumulations of coarse angular fragments with or without an admixture of finer material. The only properties they hold

* There are several notable exceptions to this principle. For instance, minerals unstable at the surface of the earth may accumulate as part of a sedimentary deposit and continue to break down after coming to rest.

in common are the size and shape of their components, and they can be described only in connection with the processes that bring about the necessary fracturing. For this reason they do not comprise a distinct group of rocks; they are placed together arbitrarily, to point out the differences that can be used to distinguish them. Table 13

TABLE 13.   Sedentary Breccias

Volcanic breccia	Craters, explosion pits, plugs and flanks of volcanoes
Enterolithic breccia	Fragments of lava crust within the parent flow
Fault and crush breccia	Faults and crush zones
Intraformational breccia	Flakes and slabs separated by shrinkage and mixed with overlying deposits
Talus breccia	Fragments loosened by weathering and accumulated at the base of steep exposures

indicates the diversity of their origins. It includes only the **sedentary** breccias, the accumulations that have not suffered transport by moving ice or water.

Volcanic Breccia

Unless they are products of a recent explosion, the fragments in a volcanic breccia are often held in place by a bonding material. If the fracturing took place in the throat of a volcano, the spaces between the blocks may have been filled by magma that rose during the eruption (Figure 20). This material is not always of the same composition as the fragments, as successive lavas erupting from a conduit may vary considerably. If the brecciation resulted from a violent explosion, the blocks may be completely disordered and mixed with debris that has avalanched down the inward slopes of the crater. Conversely, a mild shock may lead only to fracturing, so that the blocks fit loosely together as a three-dimensional but planless mosaic. Fragments that accumulate on the flanks, or at the base of a volcano tend to be mixed in a paste of volcanic ash. Unless they have been formed by a recent eruption, such mixtures are commonly indurated.

124

Enterolithic breccia is formed where a crust at the surface of a lava flow is broken and disturbed by the movement of the underlying liquid (p. 68 and Figure 10). It may include a share of foreign rock picked up along the path of a flow, but most of the fragments are similar to the congealed lava that holds them together. Usually the fragments will show signs of rapid cooling, such as glassy mar-

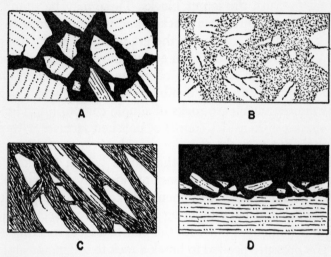

FIGURE 20. Schematic diagrams of breccias. **A,** volcanic breccia; blocks of igneous rock bound together by congealed lava (black). **B,** crush breccia, cores of rock fragments embedded in granulated matrix. **C,** fault breccia resulting from strong differential movement; the flat slabs are surrounded by gouge that has been milled in the direction of movement. **D,** intraformational breccia; slabs and flakes derived from the shrinkage of the lower deposit are incorporated in the base of the upper sediment (black).

gins and vesiculation. Structures produced by primary flow will be oriented at random, out of alignment with the flow lines in the rock considered as a unit.

Fault Breccias and Crush Breccias

The characteristics of breccias produced by directed diastrophic pressure are determined by the amount of movement that accompanied fracturing, the behavior of rock under stress, the number of movements that took place, and by whatever processes may have operated subsequently. Simple and relatively mild crushing, attended by little displacement, yields fragments of various sizes. Except that it is broken into angular formless fragments, the rock may retain its original appearance and attitude. Severe pressure can granulate brittle rocks and lead by insensible gradations to true metamorphism. At an intermediate stage the force may reduce the smaller fragments and weaker material to a granular mosaic but be insufficient to crush the larger blocks. These may be sound within but grade outward through a cracked and weakened zone to a granulated margin that merges with the granulated matrix (Figure 20).

Fault breccias that result from active movement, as distinct from the breccias of crush zones, are characterized by slickensided surfaces such as are commonly exhibited on the walls of clean sharp faults. If the fragments are rocks of simple composition (limestone, quartzite), the slickensides consist of polished surfaces with grooves or scratches. But in rocks of more complex composition, secondary minerals may develop, coating the blocks with a thin chloritic or micaceous film. This change represents an early but arrested stage of kinetic metamorphism. Fragments slickensided on opposite sides are usually flat and have tapering edges. In cross section they appear crudely lenticular, but with the polished faces meeting at sharp angles. The pressure needed to break a rock to fragments and endow them with slickensides, is enough to reduce much of the rock to powder. Hence individual pieces are usually surrounded by a matrix of **gouge,** the claylike product of differential movement (Figure 20).

Most breccias are pervious as well as porous; fluids circulate with ease through their connected fractures. Thus meteoric water may find a channel leading downward in some faults, and vapors and hot solutions ascend along others. As a result, many breccias are profoundly altered. Many are weathered to a slippery mass of clay and crumbling fragments. Water-bearing breccias are particularly troublesome in tunneling and other engineering operations. Rising fluids have various effects. They may weaken and soften the rock by hydrothermal alteration, and in many mining regions they have supplied channels for the introduction of ore-bearing solutions, so that ore deposits are concentrated in zones of fractured rock. In many breccias the fractures are closed by cementing substances. Of these, one of the most common is a limestone breccia, bound by intersecting, branching veins of calcite.

Intraformational Breccia

The surface of an argillaceous or calcareous sediment may shrink enough to crack and separate into thin slabs or flakes. Mud cracks provide the familiar example of the process, but it is difficult to determine whether exposure to the air is a prerequisite. With the deposition of a later sediment, the fragments may be shifted and disordered and mixed with the lowest part of the younger accumulation. Such mixtures are breccias only in a limited sense; more properly they are a part of the sedimentary process (Figure 20).

Talus breccia and collapse breccia both have valid places in the general category of breccias. However, the origin of most of them is so intimately involved with the chemical as well as the mechanical aspects of weathering that they are included with the weathering products on a later page of this chapter.

WEATHERING AND WEATHERING PRODUCTS

Nearly every detail that contributes to the make-up of a rock and all the elements that constitute its geographical environment have a direct influence on weathering. The most significant factors are listed below.

Topography
    Slope
    Direction of exposure
    Exposed or covered by mantle

Climate
    Annual rainfall
    Rainfall distribution
    Annual temperature
    Temperature distribution
    Diurnal temperature range

Hydrology
    Position of water table
    Surface and subsurface drainage

Biologic
    Abundance of vegetation
    Abundance of humus
    Bacterial content of soil

Rock characteristics
    Joints and other fractures
      (tightness, spacing, attitude)
    Porosity and permeability
    Planes of weakness
      (orientation and spacing of bedding, foliation)

Texture
    Coherence (bonding of minerals)
    Stability of minerals

Several of these factors call for comment. Rock exposures are common only where erosion has removed the mantle, and on slopes too steep to retain loose material. In flat regions the rate of weathering may approach or exceed the rate of erosion so that the bedrock is to some extent protected by an insulating cover of debris.

No rock, however massive and tight it may appear in the individual specimen, is free from openings. All consolidated rock is cut by joints and usually by two or more intersecting sets. Also other less conspicuous openings are almost universally present. Cavities and fractures of any kind that lead from the surface of rock toward its interior serve as channels for the entrance of air and water, the primary agents of chemical destruction.

Water plays many roles in the disruption of rocks, partly by itself, but chiefly in combination and cooperation with other substances. It combines directly with minerals (hydration) or selectively with certain ions in minerals to form new compounds. Water promotes and facilitates chemical reactions even where it does not enter the final products, and it is the necessary medium for the process of solution. It serves as the vehicle to carry oxygen, carbon dioxide, and other chemically active substances, and it is necessary for the existence of bacteria and vegetation. Where water is abundant and free to circulate, it may either remove soluble and colloidal weathering products or deposit them at a different level in the same vicinity. In regions of low temperature, its freezing leads to frost wedging. Also water is ubiquitous; the air over desert country may have a low relative humidity, but it is never dry. The hydration of minerals such as feldspar is carried on wherever air is able to penetrate.

Chemical Weathering

Chemical weathering is a complex attack, carried on simultaneously by several agents, each operating against the rock ingredients susceptible to its particular pattern of destruction. The only common rocks possessing a *relative* immunity to chemical weathering are fine textured limestones in arid regions, and pure quartzites. In general, the minerals that contain iron and those consisting of many chemical elements are the most easily decomposed.

When a mineral is altered by oxidation, hydration, or carbonation, the results are additive. Oxygen, water, and carbon dioxide are joined to ingredients already present, and there is an increase in both weight and volume. Minerals of simple composition may be transformed to a single weathering product, with nothing "left over." Thus if magnetite is transformed to either hematite or limonite, there are no by-products of the change except the energy liberated by the exothermic reaction. Thus:

$$4Fe_3O_4 + O_2 \rightarrow 6Fe_2O_3$$

and

$$4Fe_3O_4 + O_2 + 6H_2O \rightarrow 6Fe_2O_3 \cdot H_2O$$

A similar situation may arise when the destruction of a more complex mineral yields two weathering products, as in the change from anorthite to kaolin and calcite:

$$CaAl_2Si_2O_8 + CO_2 + 2H_2O \rightarrow H_4Al_2Si_2O_9 + CaCO_3$$

The place of the feldspar is taken by an intimate, chalky mixture of the two weathering products. Anorthite and kaolin have the same alumina-silica ratios, and there are no "released" products.

Kaolin is also formed by the hydration of alkali feldspar, but excess silica remains to be accounted for. The complete weathering of albite may be shown by the following (theoretical) equation:

$$2NaAlSi_3O_8 + CO_2 + H_2O \rightarrow H_4Al_2Si_2O_9 + 4SiO_2 + Na_2CO_3$$

The silica is set free as excessively fine silica particles, which in the presence of water may exist as a colloidal suspension. Also it can be removed in this form if the water is free to migrate. The reaction indicates the sodium as forming the highly soluble carbonate, but part of it might unite with silica as sodium metasilicate (Na_2SiO_3). Either of these compounds could be removed in solution. The weathering of an intermediate plagioclase may be illustrated empirically by combining the two equations above in the appropriate proportions. When potash feldspars and other potassium aluminum silicates (leucite, mica) are weathered the process is similar, except that potassium compounds are formed in place of those of sodium. Although the potash salts are even more soluble than the analogous compounds of sodium, they tend to be retained in the weathered material. Several clay minerals adsorb potassium and thus prevent its removal. It is to be emphasized that rocks can undergo a reduction of mass and volume during weathering only when substances are carried away.

The weathering of particularly complex minerals such as augite, hornblende, and biotite follows a similar pattern, but involves a larger number of elements. Table 14 lists the common products of weathering; it includes the typical minerals and the substances set free as colloids or as relatively soluble salts.

Solution

Since meteoric water contains both oxygen and carbon dioxide, no practical separation can be made between the changes just described and the solvent action of water. With a few exceptions such as halite (rock salt), rock minerals are virtually insoluble in *pure* water. However, water is a reasonably active solvent when it contains alkalies or is made slightly acid by carbon dioxide or by acid substances from decomposing organic material. The solution that takes place in any geologic process is rarely a purely physical change.

Sodium and potassium released by the weathering of preexisting minerals may go into solution in several soluble forms. In solution, they exist as positive ions (Na^+, K^+) with an appropriate balance of negative ions, possibly including CO_3^{--}, HCO_3^-, Cl^-, SO_4^{--}, and SiO_3^{--}.

Calcite and related minerals are changed to the readily soluble bicarbonates in the presence of excess carbon dioxide:

$$CaCO_3 + H_2O + CO_2 \rightleftharpoons Ca(HCO_3)_2$$

This reaction is reversible and proceeds from right to left when a rise of temperature, or any other cause, brings about a loss of carbon dioxide. It accounts for many geologic phenomena, including the (inorganic) precipitation of carbonate rocks and the ready solution of limestone. A slight change in the concentration may disturb the equilibrium and reverse the action. This is illustrated in caves by the precipitation of stalactites and stalagmites from material dissolved just a few feet above.

TABLE 14. Weathering Products

Minerals and Mixed Aggregates

"Kaolin"	Several distinct clay minerals are formed by weathering. They can be identified only by refined laboratory methods.	Formed by the hydration of aluminous minerals: feldspars, feldspathoids, micas, etc.	Highly insoluble.
Hematite	A very small percentage of finely divided hematite is sufficient to impart a deep red color to the mixtures that contain it.	Formed by the oxidation of iron-bearing minerals under relatively dry conditions.	Highly insoluble, but may be converted to relatively soluble bicarbonates under reducing conditions.
"Limonite"	Limonite is not a specific mineral, but a general term to include all mixtures of hydrated ferric oxides.	Formed by the combined effects of oxidation and hydration on iron-bearing minerals.	
Calcite		Produced by the carbonation of lime-bearing minerals.	Soluble in the presence of excess carbon dioxide.
Siderite	Seldom recognizable in weathered material.	Formed by the carbonation of iron-bearing minerals.	
Magnesite	Theoretically important, seldom recognizable.	Formed by the carbonation of magnesium-bearing minerals.	
Bauxite	Bauxite embraces various mixtures of hydrated aluminous oxides, usually with impurities, but with little silica.	Formed from aluminous minerals by long continued leaching.	Highly insoluble.

Substances Set Free in Colloidal Suspension

$Al(OH)_3$ $Fe(OH)_3$	With loss of water, both aluminum hydroxide and ferric hydroxide crystallize as fibrous aggregates. The pisolites in bauxite and limonite laterites are formed in this way.	Highly insoluble.
Colloidal silica	With partial loss of water, colloidal silica stiffens to form opal. Subsequent crystallization produces chalcedony.	

Relatively Soluble Compounds

Na_2SiO_3	Sodium metasilicate, though soluble, readily breaks down to form a silica gel, which in turn is converted to chalcedony.	
K_2CO_3	Potassium carbonate is highly soluble but is adsorbed by various clay minerals and hence may be retained in large quantity within the weathered material.	
Na_2CO_3	Sodium carbonate is less soluble than potassium carbonate but does not have the same tendency to be retained by clay.	Soluble substances are removed only if the water circulation is free. Otherwise they are retained in the weathered aggregate.
$Ca(HCO_3)_2$ $Mg(HCO_3)_2$ $Fe(HCO_3)_2$	These compounds are less soluble than the carbonates of the alkalies. They are formed in the presence of excess carbon dioxide. Ferrous bicarbonate can exist only under reducing conditions and is only slightly soluble.	
Chlorides and Sulfates	Chlorides and sulfates of magnesium and the alkalies are easily dissolved; however the chloride and sulfate ions are seldom present in sufficient abundance to form appreciable quantities of these compounds.	

131

Distribution of Released Substances

Both weathering (in the narrow sense) and solution are largely concentrated above the water table, but their effects are not uniform at different levels throughout the vadose zone. As meteoric water descends, it loses oxygen and carbon dioxide through oxidation and carbonation, so that these processes are more active in the upper part. Soluble salts and colloids may be carried downward by descending water. The abundance of water and local conditions governing circulation will determine whether they reach the water table or are arrested on the way. In regions of low rainfall they may be concentrated near the surface or drawn upward through capillary openings, and in extremely dry climates they may be held in place where they were formed.

No single rule can be formulated to include the conditions bringing about the precipitation of dissolved substances and the deposition of material carried in suspension. The widespread occurrence of calcite as cement in detrital sediments and as a vein mineral attests not only to the abundance of this compound but also to the ease with which calcium bicarbonate is converted to calcite. Sodium salts are precipitated under normal circumstances only by the evaporation of the solvent, otherwise they find their way to their ultimate destination, the sea.

Suspended silica is the most abundant colloid set free by weathering. When it loses sufficient water it stiffens and congeals to form opaline silica, and this, in turn, readily crystallizes as chalcedony. This is the origin of much chert, chalcedony crusts, silicious cements, and vein material. When chalcedony contains a small fraction of ferruginous matter, it forms the various red and brown silicious mixtures known collectively as jasper. Colloidal ferric hydroxide, $Fe(OH)_3$, undergoes a similar history, forming crusts and fillings of limonite that are changed to hematite by dehydration. Minerals that have crystallized from a collodial state usually consist of closely packed, fibrous crystals. When these form a crust or line a cavity, they are usually parallel, with the long axes perpendicular to the plane of attachment and with their outer ends terminating as a smooth, botryoidal surface. The pisolites in bauxite and lateritic iron ore consist of similar fibrous crystals arranged radially.

Altered Rocks

Oxidation and Reduction

Wherever rock debris and rock surfaces are stained by the characteristic reds and brown of hematite and limonite, it is safe to assume that oxidizing conditions prevail and that sufficient oxygen is present to keep the iron compounds in the ferric state. This applies to weathering products in all situations, whether in place, or during transport, or after they have been deposited. The absence of these typical colors may mean that the material is free from iron or that the iron oxides have been reduced to ferrous compounds. In the zone of weathering, reduction proceeds only where there are large amounts of decomposing organic material. The oxidation of some carbon compounds is a sufficiently active process to remove oxygen from the ferric oxides. The procedure is understood only in a general way, and it is not known what ferrous compounds may result directly from the reaction. However, it would be reasonable to expect ferrous carbonate to be an abundant substance and ferrous sulfate and ferrous silicate to form in the presence of the necessary sulfur compounds and available silica. In the following symbolic equation, the organic compounds are represented by carbon and the oxidized carbon compound as carbon dioxide. Ferrous oxide symbolizes an intermediate step in the reaction, but it would not occur in nature.

$$
\begin{aligned}
\text{I} \qquad & 2Fe_2O_3 + C \rightarrow 4FeO + CO_2 \\
\text{II} \qquad & FeO + CO_2 \rightarrow FeCO_3
\end{aligned}
$$

Analogous but similarly hypothetical equations can be written to indicate the formation of iron silicates and sulfates. Ferrous carbonate, like calcite, is changed to the more soluble bicarbonate in the presence of carbon dioxide:

$$ FeCO_3 + CO_2 + H_2O \rightarrow Fe(HCO_3)_2 $$

Organisms and Organic Substances

The direct role of plants in weathering is limited to the mechanical action that ensues when roots, growing in joints or other spaces, expand enough to enlarge the crack or to break the rock apart. The chemical effect of plants is considerable, but indirect, and results from the decomposition of dead tissue rather than by the activity of living organisms. Decaying vegetation produces various organic acids that have a strong solvent action. Thus coal-making swamps are underlaid by **fire clay,** a clay made refractory by the dissolving and removal of the alkalies. Similarly the soils under tropical rain forests are notoriously barren because all but the most insoluble substances have been carried away. The reducing action of organic material was considered in the previous section.

Plants can exist within a wide range of temperature, provided their roots can find water and a foothold. They grow most luxuriantly in humid climates. The chemical effect depends upon the amount of humus that accumulates. Plant decay is brought about by various kinds of bacteria, some acting on woody matter, others attacking different tissues. Wherever conditions are highly favorable for bacteria, they keep the humus at a minimum, oxidation is the dominant process, and the soil is strongly colored by hematite or limonite. Bacteria, like the higher plants, are encouraged by warmth and moisture, but they are more sensitive to cold. Hence in high latitudes and high altitudes, humus accumulates faster than bacteria can break it down. In these places the ferric oxides are reduced and the ground is colored gray or black from the admixed humus. Bacterial action is also retarded in wet regions that are poorly drained. In swamps, ponds, and even shallow seas, the acid by-products of decay become concentrated to a degree that limits the work of many kinds of bacteria. Also the oxidation of organic compounds removes dissolved oxygen from the water so that only anaerobic bacteria can continue to function. It is for these reasons that the soils of swamps and marshes characteristically consist of plastic black mixtures of clay and carbonaceous matter. In tropical countries red soil may form on slopes with adequate drainage, while the soils of nearby swamps are black.

It has been suspected that bacteria may be responsible for some weathering, either directly or by acting as catalysts, but this has not yet been demonstrated.

Temperature and Temperature Changes

Ordinary chemical reactions are accelerated by higher temperatures. On the average, each increase of $10°$ C doubles the reaction rate. While this does not hold for every reaction, it is equally valid for the swift transformations of the laboratory, and the extraordinarily slow rates that govern many geologic processes. Also most chemical changes are facilitated by water, as it brings about a more intimate mingling of the reacting substances that can take place in the dry state. For these two reasons, chemical weathering is most rapid in tropical and semitropical regions.

For many years it was assumed that the mechanical disruption of rocks could be brought about by the differential expansion of minerals subjected to sudden heating and cooling. The crumbling of rock in the desert was explained by the wide difference of temperature between early morning and mid-afternoon. In experiments performed by Dr. D. T. Griggs, rock was exposed to temperature changes far greater and far more frequent than those imposed by nature but showed no appreciable weakening, even though the experiment was continued over a long interval. Apparently the expansion and contraction of minerals is a contributing factor in the destruction of rocks, but one that becomes significant only when it accompanies chemical attack.

The increase in volume that attends chemical weathering results in stresses between minerals. For instance, when anorthite is completely converted to kaolin and calcite, the gain in volume is thirty-six per cent, as shown in the following computation:

	anorthite $\rightarrow$ $CaAl_2Si_2O_8$	kaolin $H_4Al_2Si_2O_9$	$+$	calcite $CaCO_3$
Molecular weights	278	258		100
To 100%	100	92.8		36
Weight increase		28.8%		
Specific gravity	2.76	2.6		2.72
Relative volumes	100.8	99.3		36.8
To 100%	100	98.5		37.7
Volume increase		36.2%		

The actual increase would be even greater, since weathering products are mixed and finely divided and so require more space than coarser homogenous minerals. Other complex minerals suffer comparable changes. Diminution of volume takes place only when soluble or colloidal substances are removed.

The spalling of thin weathered shells, exfoliation on a small scale, appears to be governed by volume changes of both types. Chemical attack, concentrated upon the exposed surface of a rock, changes the volumes of minerals and weakens the bonds between them. At the same time, the low heat conductivity of rock limits diurnal expansion and contraction to a thin outer rind, a shell of altered rock that is alternately tightened and loosened until it separates from the rock within.

In climates where water freezes and especially where temperatures fluctuate about the freezing point, ice wedging is an active process. Its operation depends upon the increase in volume that attends the change from water to ice. (The specific gravity of ice at

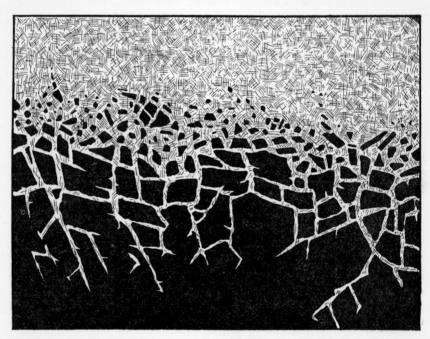

FIGURE 21. Shattering of rock by ice-wedging. Melt water from the ice above penetrates crevices in the rock (black) and freezes to form veins of ice. This process widens and lengthens the openings, and the continued wedging results in an intimate mixture of rock fragments and ice.

136

atmospheric pressure and O° C is 0.918, hence the volume of a gram of ice is 1.09 cc, which represents a volume increase of nine per cent.) Water, freezing in a crevice, enlarges the opening by pressure against the sides and drives the crack deeper by the wedging action. The most conspicuous effects of this process are formed in the immediate vicinity of bodies of ice and persistent snowbanks. Water, released by melting, enters whatever spaces are available, and upon freezing it again forms veins of ice. These may be connected with the ice from which the water escaped. Intermittent prying action enlarges the veins, and further splitting of the rock leads to the development of branching distributaries of ice. Ultimately a transitional zone of mixed ice and rock fragments intervenes between bedrock and the adjacent ice body (Figure 21). The intimate shattering produced in this way is known as **nivation.** Ice wedging is perhaps the only phase of weathering by which rocks are broken up through the action of temperature changes alone.

Other Climatic Factors

Because the general aspect of the landscape and the topographic details of arid regions are so strikingly different from those that obtain in humid lands, there is danger of overestimating the dissimilarities of weathering in contrasted climates. Except for the absence of the direct and indirect influence of vegetation in dry places, there is little qualitative difference; minerals and rocks are destroyed in the same ways. However, both the quantitative effect of contributing processes and the subsequent fate of the products vary greatly. Active weathering is largely concentrated above the water table; in regions of abundant rainfall this is a relatively shallow zone, in dry country it is deeper and often undetermined. In some deserts weathering appears to reach considerable depths, apparently continuing where spaces are invaded by air but are too small to permit the entrance of water. The kaolinization of feldspar to considerable depths in dry country suggests that hydration can be brought about by the water vapor in air, without requiring the presence of liquid water.

Descending water loses its dissolved oxygen and carbon dioxide through oxidation and carbonation, so that at lower levels weather-

137

ing is largely restricted to hydration and solution. Where it circulates freely, water removes soluble and finely divided matter and so decreases the mass and volume of the weathered mixture. If rainfall is scant these substances remain where they were formed and so contribute to a maximum volume increase. Otherwise they may be carried downward and redeposited, or else they are drawn upward along capillary openings to form a crust or a powder at the surface.

In regions of recent glaciation most rocks are weathered only on exposed surfaces and along fractures penetrated by water. When broken open, unaltered rock is revealed below a (usually) thin and contrasted weathered crust. Apparently in most places the decayed rock was removed by glacial action, and the time that has elapsed since is too short for deep weathering. Another exception is seen in tropical climates where high temperature combines with an abundance of water to produce a deep and intense chemical weathering.

SEDENTARY DEPOSITS

Talus

Except where the local rock consists of loosely cemented grains, talus slopes are accumulations of rock fragments rather than individual minerals. Also the kinds of rocks and minerals are limited to the types exposed in the outcrops above. The effects of structure and climate in determining weathering are particularly conspicuous. If widely spaced joints or bedding planes control weathering, the talus debris will include large blocks showing at least one plane surface. Similarly, thin bedded rocks produce flat slabs. In humid regions the fragments may be mixed with soil and the surface covered by vegetation, so that even if the slope is excessively steep, it may be anchored and stable. Conversely, where vegetation is absent, the surface of the talus slope is loose and often stands precariously balanced at the angle of repose. Coarse-grained rocks such as granite and gneiss disintegrate under an arid climate to a characteristic rubble. This consists of weathered and partly weathered minerals, either separate or loosely clinging together as rough and friable fragments. Fine-textured rocks seldom break down as free mineral particles.

Criteria for the recognition of talus breccia are needed only when it is seen apart from its place of origin in the present geomorphic cycle. Clues to the determination of an ancient talus breccia, or of this material removed from its site, are:

1. Angular, unsorted fragments
2. Fragments limited to either one or a few rock types
3. Fragments varied in size, shape, and degree of weathering
4. Contrasted degrees of weathering on different sides of the same block
5. Absence of smooth or polished surfaces

The open texture of talus encourages weathering and facilitates the work of circulating water. Hence some breccias may be cemented in place. This applies particularly to limestone and calcareous shale. Calcite, dissolved from these rocks may precipitate to attach the newly fallen blocks, so that the entire accumulation is firmly bound together.

Residual Soil

Residual soils may be distinguished from those carried in by moving media through the following characteristics:

1. Residual soils are devoid of stratification. The soil passes gradually to the bedrock below without a definite contact.
2. Rock fragments and mineral grains are those of the bedrock.
3. Rock fragments are larger and less weathered from the surface downward.
4. Unless the contributing rock is conglomerate, the fragments will show no evidence of abrasion.

The physical and mineralogical make-up of a residual soil depends upon the character of the parent rock and the kind and degree of weathering. A soil recently formed will be rich in incompletely weathered rock fragments. One exposed for a long interval will contain few if any fragments and the sand size particles will be limited to quartz and similarly stable minerals. Such soils are usually deep and consist preponderately of clay size material. Plasticity is determined by the abundance of colloids, either of mineral or organic origin.

The colors of soils range from white to black, through almost every intermediate shade of gray, yellow, red, and brown. The controlling factors are iron content, its state of oxidation, and the relative abundance of humus.

Laterites

Laterites are deposits consisting only of the most insoluble mineral substances; residual bodies formed by chemical weathering and leaching carried on to the penultimate stage. To attain this condition requires a long interval of time, a situation favorable for intense chemical weathering, and topography, where erosion is at a minimum. These conditions are fulfilled in flat regions of heavy rainfall, as for instance on the low divides that separate the valley floors of a peneplane. However, in tropical countries the high temperatures may so accelerate chemical processes that less time is required, and laterite may form at higher levels.

With sufficient water, leaching removes the more soluble materials, the alkalies and carbonates, as these are set free by the decomposition of the complex silicates. Then later, and more slowly, quartz is dissolved and carried away, and the clay minerals are further decomposed. In typical laterite only silica and the hydrated oxides of iron and aluminum remain in appreciable quantity. When these are first set free from their parent minerals, they probably exist as colloids. In many laterites they subsequently crystallize in the spherical aggregates known as pisolites. These structures embedded in a fine earthy matrix are the most typical characteristics of laterites.

Economically valuable laterites are of two kinds, limonite (including some manganese deposits) and bauxite. Each of these must be low in silica and relatively free of the other. Both limonite and the aluminum oxides are less vulnerable to leaching than silica and may be produced from rocks with fair quantities of iron or aluminum. In general, bauxite is formed from aluminous rocks that were originally iron-poor, or from which the iron has been dissolved after its oxides have been reduced by organic matter to the relatively soluble ferrous compounds. Limonitic iron ore is mostly derived from femic rocks poor in aluminum.

Altered Rocks

DEUTERIC AND HYDROTHERMAL ALTERATION

Deuteric alteration is an attack, only partly destructive, produced within an igneous body by residual fluids that have been trapped by the hardening of the rock. Its effects are plainly visible in hand specimens only where they have progressed to an extreme stage. There it is manifested by the breaking down of feldspar, especially plagioclase, and the making over of femic minerals. The feldspar is changed to clay minerals and finely divided muscovite (sericite) or to epidote. Biotite is converted to chlorite, and the nonaluminous femic minerals (olivine and some pyroxenes) to serpentine. Rocks so affected are softened and the surfaces feel soapy to the touch from the clay minerals and chlorite. The rocks have a dull somewhat earthy appearance. They may be gray, or gray-green from chlorite or be mottled by patches of the familiar yellow green of epidote. In these particulars they resemble the rocks affected by hydrothermal alteration, which in many respects is a similar attack. However deuteric alteration is confined by definition to changes within an igneous rock brought about by its own fluids, whereas hydrothermal alteration may take place in any rock susceptible to the influence of hot water. Hand specimen study will seldom suffice to determine which type of alteration has brought about the softening and weakening that is commonly observed in lava flows. Both types of alteration can be distinguished from weathering by the absence of staining by hematite and limonite, unless these minerals have developed later through oxidizing processes.

Hydrothermal alteration is largely confined to the vicinity of igneous activity and is especially noticeable in the wall rock that encloses mineral veins. The hot water, or water vapor, which is the main agent of change may come directly as an emanation from an igneous source or may be ground water heated locally. The rocks most vulnerable are those containing femic minerals and intermediate or calcic plagioclase. Hence the femic igneous rocks, and schists and gneisses with biotite, amphibole, and pyroxene are often altered. Minerals resulting from hydrothermal alteration are: serpentine, chlorite, talc, epidote, "clay minerals," and sericite. Since hot water is a powerful dissolving agent the alteration process may be complicated by the removal of some minerals, or compounds, and the emplacement of others. This may but need not proceed as replacement. Thus it commonly happens that pyrite and quartz are introduced, sodium tends to be removed, and potassium added. The only distinctive rocks formed by hydrothermal alteration are (some) serpentines, and **soapstone.** The latter is a nonfoliate mixture of talc with other minerals. Both of these rocks are commonly regarded as metamorphic products. However, this is a matter of terminology rather than origin.

SUGGESTIONS FOR STUDY

1. Compare samples of breccia of different origins as to:
   a. Composition of fragments (mixed or uniform).
   b. Fragment shapes and surface features.
   c. Arrangement of fragments.
   d. Cementing material or matrix.
   e. Porosity.
2. Much can be learned about a soil by stirring a sample vigorously in water, and pouring off the suspended particles before they have time to settle. The process should be repeated until the water is clear. One may then examine the remaining fraction for sizes, shapes, and the identification of rock and mineral fragments. If the muddy fraction is decanted into a glass jar, it will gradually clear, with the relatively coarser and heavier particles (usually silt) below the clay. If approximately quantitative results are desired, they may be secured by drying and weighing the original sample, and whatever fractions are subsequently separated.
3. The changes of weight and volume that attend the weathering of anorthite to kaolin and calcite are computed on p. 135. Similar computations with other minerals serve to emphasize the qualitative and (approximately) quantitative aspects of chemical weathering.
4. The order of concentration required to produce a deposit of lateritic limonite can be obtained by assuming that basalt, of the average composition given in Table 9, is leached until only limonite remains. (Compare the weight of the iron, computed as goethite, $Fe_2O_3 \cdot H_2O$, to 100 units by weight of the original rock.) An analogous calculation, beginning with the nepheline syenite in Table 9, will show the amount

142

of bauxite that theoretically might be left by the lateritic weathering of an aluminum-rich rock. (Compute bauxite as consisting of $Al_2O_3 \cdot 2H_2O$.) Neither of these examples takes into account the iron or aluminum removed during the weathering process, or the impurities which always remain in natural laterites; they are useful to show the maximum ratio of ore minerals to the parent rock.

·8·

Sedimentary Rocks

THE rocks considered in this chapter include those that have been carried in from elsewhere by moving water, air, or ice, also those chemically precipitated from surface waters and accumulations of organic matter. Nearly all of them consist of transported material, and most of them are stratified. Typical exceptions are coal and till, respectively. As the term *sedimentary* is customarily employed, it embraces all rocks formed by surface processes, as distinct from the products of volcanism and diastrophism. For the sedentary materials described in the previous chapter there is no name in general use. They also may properly be regarded as sedimentary; their separation from the transported and precipitated rocks is abitrary and is used to facilitate description.

The first necessary step in the study of any rock is to examine its constituents and its bulk properties, and to observe and record all the details that are visible. This is the prerequisite to identification and interpretation and is the same for rocks of any origin. Although the procedure is alike for all rocks, the questions that are involved in the identification and interpretation of sedimentary rocks are distinctly different from those imposed by a study of igneous material. These differences arise partly from the dissimilarity of origin, but perhaps even more from a difference in emphasis; investigations that deal with igneous rocks, and those concerned with sedimentary geology are usually undertaken with entirely different objectives. These and the differences introduced by genetic factors are explained in the following account.

144

Sedimentary Rocks

Variable Factors

An igneous rock, viewed as a single specimen or within the limits of a single outcrop may be heterogeneous in that it contains different minerals or consists of a mixture of crystals and glass, but it is nevertheless a single substance, produced by the cooling of a presumably homogeneous liquid. This is the common case, although rocks with xenoliths or other contamination may be met. Magmas and lavas are predominantly silicious solutions, and although their compositions vary, only a few substances are present in appreciable amounts. Furthermore, the chemical differences exhibited in magmas and lavas occur within a narrow range; only an extremely small fraction of the mathematically possible combinations actually exists. Even though an igneous rock is a complex substance, nevertheless it is essentially the product of a single process, the cooling of a silicious liquid. In igneous petrology the paramount questions are: (1) the identification of the rock through the identification of its minerals and their textural arrangement, and at times, from its chemical composition, and (2) the interpretation, from these data, of the sequence of physical and chemical events that occurred during its emplacement and cooling. In many investigations of igneous rocks the environment is considered important only to the extent that it may have influenced the composition and the cooling process. This restriction would not apply, however, to a study of ore deposits or any endeavor concerned with the relationships between rocks.

The sedimentary rocks embrace a much larger number of ingredients, including all but the least stable substances formed by igneous activity and much else beside. Even though they are assembled under the narrow range of temperature and pressure that prevails on the lands and the sea floor, the make-up of sedimentary rocks is controlled by a much larger number of variable factors than enter into igneous history. Since a large part of all sedimentary matter consists of substances produced by the weathering of preexisting rocks, all of the factors involved in weathering (p. 127) have an influence on the sedimentary rocks. To these must be added the geographic elements that determine the transport and deposition of rock waste by moving media.

In addition to mechanically deposited rock detritus, sedimentary rocks include substance precipitated from solutions by organisms, by inorganic chemical reactions, by the evaporation of water, and accumulations of organic tissue. The presence, abundance, and character of the materials formed by these processes is narrowly determined by the local environment, particularly the topography and climate. Another set of variables is introduced by the later history of the deposits; the manner and degree of lithification, and the extent to which reorganization has taken place. The diversity of the elements that determine the characteristics of sedimentary rocks is indicated in Table 15.

From these considerations it is a necessary conclusion that the compositions of sedimentary rocks are far more diverse than the products of volcanism. Also this variability is greatly increased by mixing; detritus from different sources may be mingled with chemically deposited minerals in any proportions. Some rocks, till is an example, are notoriously heterogeneous, but on the other hand, relatively "pure" rocks are far more common and abundant than monomineralic igneous rocks. Limestones containing little but calcite and sands with more than ninety per cent quartz are not difficult to explain, whereas dunite and anorthosite are rare and exceptional rocks.

Interpretation

Sedimentary rocks are studied for various immediate purposes, but if these studies are pursued far, they lead toward an end that is the ultimate goal of geology—to an explanation of the constitution of the earth's outer shell in terms of geologic processes. To this the sediments lend themselves far more readily than do the igneous and metamorphic rocks. Deposition takes place at the surface of the earth, where much of it can be observed directly, whereas the forces and movements responsible for volcanism and diastrophism are not only hidden but also involve combinations of pressure and temperature as yet unavailable in the laboratory. Furthermore, sedimentary rocks cover most of the land and so are readily accessible, and when well exposed, a sedimentary rock can be examined through its complete thickness.

The chief task of the sedimentary petrologist and an increasing number of stratigraphers is interpretation—the restoration of the

TABLE 15. Genetic Factors in Sedimentary Rocks

Variable Factors	Properties Affected
Source area	
relief	These factors exert their influence
stability	by controlling weathering, ero-
climate	sion, and transport
Source material	
composition	Composition, grain size, color
texture	
structure	
coherence	grain size
Weathering, fragmentation	
type	
degree	Grain size, composition, color
Erosion and transport	
agency (wind, ice, water)	Grain size
time and distance	Rounding
velocity	Sorting
Depositional environment (subaerial deposits)	
topography	
drainage	
climate	
position of water table	Composition
stability (whether subsiding)	Grain size
Depositional environment (water-laid deposits)	Sorting
depth	Color
stability	Stratification
temperature	Organic content
salinity	Porosity
circulation (waves, currents)	Crystallinity
aeration	
Subsequent history	
burial, pressure	
exposure (to air, fresh or salt water)	Porosity
movement	Induration (compaction)
fracturing	Cementing
compaction	Crystallinity
	Concretions
	Color, etc.

conditions under which the rock was deposited. The evidence submitted by a rock, through its composition, texture, its contents and its structure, is used to reconstruct the geographic provenance of the original deposit. The recent emphasis on this aspect of geology has stimulated a vigorous reexamination of present day deposition, so

that **sedimentation** and **sedimentary ecology** have become conspicuously active studies.

The interpretation of the past environment of a rock from its
chemical and physical characteristics requires caution no less than
imagination. It can be undertaken safely only when a suite of specimens is available, or better, when the rocks can be examined in the
field. For just as a single sentence, taken out of its context in a
speech or article, can be used by a controversialist to pervert the
meaning of his opponent, so also an isolated rock specimen may give
a false or misleading impression.

Nomenclature and Classification

Even though the sedimentary rocks are products of many variable
genetic factors and include an almost endless variety of mixtures,
nevertheless the different types have received many fewer names
than are found in the accounts of igneous rocks. Also the names most
often used are employed loosely and many describe only a single
characteristic. Thus *limestone* signifies only the mineralogical composition of a rock, and the term *sandstone* reveals nothing about a
rock except its texture. When using these names it is necessary to
employ various qualifying adjectives to avoid ambiguity. For instance, *oolitic* limestone and *feldspathic* sandstone convey much
more definite information about the rocks in question. The various
qualifying terms most commonly used are listed in Table 16. There
are a few names that connote distinctive characteristics. Thus *coquina, loess, chalk,* and *tillite* are terms that restrict the rocks so
designated within certain limits of origin or components.

For sedimentary rocks there is no generally accepted standard
classification. This lack becomes increasingly serious as more refined
studies lead to more and more detailed information. Several noteworthy systems have been presented, not only to provide a logical
classification but also to fix the meanings of rock names now used
and to supply precisely defined terms for the obvious gaps. Among
these, the most recent is that of Professor P. D. Krynine.* This sys-

---

* "The Megascopic Study and Field Classification of Sedimentary Rocks," *Journal
of Geology,* Vol. 56, No. 2 1948, pp. 130–165. This paper can also be obtained separately, as *Technical Paper 130* of the Pennsylvania State College Mineral Industries
Station. It should be studied carefully by every student who expects to work with
rocks.

TABLE 16. Descriptive Terms Applied to Sediments

Composition

Calcareous	Containing an appreciable amount of calcium carbonate
Dolomitic	Consisting essentially of dolomite rather than calcite
Magnesian	Intermediate in composition between calcite and dolomite
Quartzose	Applies to sandstone and conglomerate consisting mostly of quartz
Silicious	Containing appreciable amounts of quartz or other silicates
Cherty	Containing chert nodules or replacements
Feldspathic	Feldspar grains are conspicuous fragments
Arkosic	Sandstone and conglomerate with appreciable feldspar
Ferruginous	With sufficient hematite or limonite to be colored by these minerals
Carbonaceous	Containing sufficient organic matter to be dark gray or black
Argillaceous	With appreciable amounts of clay minerals

Texture

Rudaceous,	Psephitic	Fragments coarser than sand
Arenaceous,	Psammitic	Sand-size particles
Lutaceous,	Pelitic	Particles finer than silt
Crystalline		

Origin and Environment

Biogenic	Formed directly through action of organisms
Hydrogenic	Precipitated from water by inorganic processes
Hydroclastic	Rocks consisting of discrete particles deposited in water
Pyroclastic	Fragments produced by volcanic explosions
Eolian	Transported and deposited by wind
Aqueous	Deposited in water
Terrigenous	Derived from the land
Lacustrine	Lake deposits
Marine	Deposited in sea water
Continental	Deposited on the lands
Allogenic	Introduced from without the deposit
Authigenic	Formed or reorganized within the deposit

Strength, Coherence

Friable	Crumbles readily
Indurated	Hardened
Fissile	Splits easily parallel to bedding

Structure

Oolitic	
Concretionary	
Laminated	In thin bands or layers

149

tem of classification and nomenclature is based primarily on the two most fundamental properties, texture and composition. For some purposes, the mode of origin and conditions of deposition are no less important than the physical and chemical make-up, and they have the merit of being genetic factors. However, any rock classification that takes account of several variables is cumbersome, requiring a too large number of separate categories and the invention of too many names. Also a system that includes place and mode of deposition as well as the visible characteristics presumes that these additional factors can be determined.

Diagenesis

The formation of an igneous rock is a process of solidification; liquid is converted to firm rock. In the history of a sedimentary rock there is no point that corresponds to the consolidation of magma. Sedimentary material, with only a few exceptions, is deposited as a loose aggregate, subject to a variety of later changes. Lithification is only one of the possible modifications and it may be preceded and followed by others. No single process or event can be selected as final. For instance, when pebbles come to rest to form a bed of gravel, the primary act of deposition is completed and the gravel layer is a definite, recognizable unit of rock. However, the pebbles can be expected to undergo an indefinite amount of settling, and if more gravel or another sediment is added above, the pebbles will be pressed into a more compact fit. When water enters the pore space, it may introduce cementing materials, or bring about replacement, or dissolve and remove some ingredients. Rocks of different composition and habit are susceptible to other types of change. The history of a sedimentary rock is completed only when, *within a given and temporarily stable environment,* no further changes or adjustments are taking place. This applies only to the history of a rock in its formative stages and not to subsequent changes such as metamorphism or weathering.

The changes that occur within sedimentary accumulations are known collectively as **diagenesis.** This term has been used with several differently restricted meanings, but is applied here to all the physical and chemical modifications that take place, either after deposition, or while deposition is still in progress. The various diagenetic effects are achieved by:

Mechanical compaction
Dehydration
Crystallization of colloids
Recombination to form new compounds ⎫
Changes in texture ⎬ recrystallization
Introduction of minerals and colloids ⎭
Replacement

The physical and chemical properties of a sediment determine its susceptibility to change. Most detrital deposits are loose; the application of even relatively light pressure brings about a tighter packing, and if they are fine grained the pressure will squeeze out a large part of the mechanically trapped water. Some clay substances, when forced together, have a tendency to cohere. Water is also removed by an increase in temperature. A large part of sedimentary material consists of weathering products, some of which are stable only under surface conditions. This applies particularly to clay minerals which are readily changed by pressure to micaceous and chloritic minerals. The original constituents of both clastic and chemical deposits may include substances in colloidal suspension, and colloids are frequently introduced. Inorganic colloids crystallize readily through loss of water, usually to form excessively fine, fibrous crystals. These in turn may change into other minerals, usually of a coarser texture, either as a result of pressure, or because of further loss of water. Common examples are:

opal → chalcedony → quartz
ferric hydroxide → goethite ⇄ hematite

All predominantly detrital deposits are porous, and in the coarser sediments the openings are large enough and sufficiently connected to invite the entrance and permit the flow of water and other fluids. The principal effects of circulating water are, as indicated previously, to introduce new substances, to remove others, and through the simultaneous operation of both processes to bring about replacement.

151

TABLE 17.   Sedimentary Rock Constituents

Primary Substances	
Detrital Constituents	Chemical Precipitates
Lithic Fragments	Calcite, other carbonates
quartzite	Opal, chalcedony (quartz?)
granite, etc.	Colloidal limonite
gneiss, etc.	Hematite
schist, phyllite, slate	Glauconite
sandstone	Carbonaceous material
coarse pyroclastics (volcanic bombs,	Halite
blocks)	Gypsum
glass shards	Anhydrite
Mineral grains and finer particles	
quartz	
chalcedony, chert, jasper	
feldspar	
muscovite	
magnetite, ilmenite	
garnet	
hornblende, pyroxene	
clay minerals	
rock flour	
volcanic ash	

Secondary Substances	
Introduced	Reorganization Products
Opal, chalcedony	Quartz
Quartz	Hematite
Carbonates	Micaceous minerals
Gypsum	Chlorite
Hydrated iron oxides	Dolomite
	Anhydrite
	Pyrite
	Graphite
	Glauconite (?)

Among the ingredients of sedimentary rocks calcite is abundant, both as a primary and introduced mineral. It calls for particular attention because of all the common minerals it is the most conspicuous in its adaptations to chemical and physical changes. Finely divided calcite, subjected to pressure, is converted easily to visibly crystalline matter, and under strong orogenic pressure it will flow to conform with the available space. Its relatively high solubility facilitates its removal from one place and transfer to another, and renders it susceptible to replacement. Fractured calcite provides its own material to heal the break. At temperatures approaching metamorphism, calcite unites with other minerals to produce lime silicates.

The common minerals that result from diagenesis are listed in the lower part of Table 17. A distinction is sometimes made between **allogenic** minerals, those that have been added from without, and **authigenic** minerals, formed by the reorganization of material already present. If these terms are used, they should be applied only where there is clear evidence to support the origin that they imply. **Recrystallization** means that crystalline material has suffered a change in crystal form, and hence in its texture, or that the elements in previous crystals have been regrouped to form new crystalline compounds. Thus the changes from chalcedony to quartz, from fine to visibly crystalline calcite, and from clay to mica are authentic examples of recrystallization, but the crystallization of opal to form chalcedony is not. With the exception of removal by solution and some replacement exchanges, the processes of diagenesis tend toward the lithification of the rocks involved.

CLASTIC SEDIMENTS

Rocks consisting predominantly of discrete particles constitute by far the largest part of sedimentary material. These are the deposits that are familiar as gravel, sand, and clay when unconsolidated, and as conglomerate, sandstone, and shale in their indurated state. All these terms are vague because they refer to the sizes of fragments only, without specifying the limits. Also the names have no genetic significance, as any of the rocks designated by them may be deposited under a variety of conditions. Nevertheless, these terms are firmly rooted in geological language and designate a conspicuous feature; they provide a convenient point of departure for description and explanation.

Grain Size

Transported particles are named according to their size: *boulder, cobble, pebble, granule, sand, silt,* and *clay.* All these except granule are names that have entered geology from our common speech and have retained their everyday meanings. However, in defining them for scientific work, different authorities* have established different diameters to set apart the separate sizes. In studies of sedimentation, statistical analysis of grain size has become the investigators' chief tool. In this work little emphasis is placed on names, and a given **grade** is designated by the maximum and minimum dimensions of the diameter of the particles. Grains are separated according to size by passing them through a series of sieves with progressively smaller openings, so that the fraction retained on any one sieve includes the particles fine enough to have passed through the sieve above, but too large to pass downward to the next.

In less specialized work, the names *boulder, cobble,* and *pebble* can be used with their ordinary connotations, without serious danger of their being misunderstood. (A pebble is the size convenient for a missile, cobbles are larger but can be picked up with one hand. Anything bigger is a boulder.) However, the description of a rock containing them should include measurements of their diameters, and, if it is practicable, an estimate of their average size. Smaller particles must be named with more care and accompanied by a brief explanation of the criteria used to describe them. A diameter of two millimeters is generally accepted as separating coarse sand from fine pebbles (or granules). Various limits have been set for silt and fine sand; nevertheless in megascopic, nonstatistical work, particles can be described as sand if they are visible without a lens and as silt if they are smaller than this, but feel gritty when rubbed between the fingers. The sizes of sand grains can be estimated with sufficient accuracy for ordinary purposes if a loose sample is spread out on squared millimeter paper and examined with a lens.

Classification of sizes by such qualitative methods introduces the observer as a variable factor. The inaccuracy inherent in this proce-

* For a recent summary and discussion of terminology and standards, see *Sedimentary Rocks* by F. J. Pettijohn, Harper & Brothers, New York, 1949.

dure can be partly overcome by using sieved samples as a standard. The observer should examine each grade to determine the smallest size that permits him:

1. To identify minerals with conspicuous properties.
2. To observe the shapes of fragments.
3. To see individual particles without a lens.
4. To see individual particles with a lens of given magnification.

The determination of grain size is seldom simple, because few sediments are so well sorted as to be homogeneous in texture, and it is desirable to indicate the size variations and to estimate, as far as possible, the relative amounts of the sizes that are present. The task becomes even more difficult and the description even less precise when examining rocks that are too firmly indurated for separation into their component grains.

Effects of Abrasion

The shapes of fragments indicate roughly the amount of abrasion they have undergone in transport by moving air or water. In general, for particles of any single size, the roundness increases with the violence, the distance, or the time of handling. A freshly broken fragment, showing no signs of abrasion, may be described as *sharply angular* if it displays sharp edges and corners. The first effect of abrasion is to blunt these projections, without changing the general shape, and the fragment becomes *angular*. It is *subangular* if it retains surfaces that are flat or slightly concave, suggesting something of its original form. Even with long-continued wear, fragments seldom approach a spherical shape, although many become ovoid (egg shaped) or ellipsoidal. They are *well rounded* when no edges, corners, or conspicuously flat original surfaces remain.

Although these terms are not precise and lead to disagreement in classifying borderline fragments, they are nevertheless easily understood, and two observers will seldom differ seriously in describing the shape exhibited by the particles within a given limit of size and composition in the same sample.

On the average, large fragments are more thoroughly rounded than smaller sized fragments, because they can be transported only by swiftly moving currents and their kinetic energy is correspond-

155

ingly large. Furthermore they travel along the bottom with the maximum opportunity for collisions, scraping, and grinding. Conversely, particles small enough to be carried in suspension suffer almost no abrasion. Silt is angular, and much of it sharp. The shape observed in sand and pebbles is not necessarily the effect of its most recent transportation, for the same material may be reworked and redistributed during several geomorphic cycles without erasing the effects of the earlier abrasion.

Apart from rounding, the shapes of fragments may be influenced by structure, particularly by planes of weakness such as cleavage, foliation, and bedding. Mica is always transported and deposited as flat flakes; grains of hornblende are often long and narrow because of the prismatic cleavage. Similarly, closely bedded shales and fine-grained foliates may break down to thin flat pebbles. The marked inequidimensional form of such fragments is independent of the degree of rounding; their ends and edges may show any degree of sharpness or wear. The distinction between the effects of abrasion and the relative dimensions of fragments is made by taking account of their **sphericity,** the extent to which they approach a spherical form. Except in specialized studies, it is necessary to record this factor only in fragments that are notably flat or elongate.

When some rocks and minerals reach the well-rounded stage, their surfaces may be smoothed to a high polish. The controlling factors are hardness and tenacity in minerals, and hardness, fine texture, and homogeneity in rocks. The effects of differential abrasion are conspicuous on the surfaces of coarse-textured rocks such as granite and gneiss; streaks and patches of quartz are polished and stand out as low ridges and mounds, whereas the softer femic minerals are exposed in low and roughened pits.

GRAVEL AND CONGLOMERATE

Lithology

The only agents capable of transporting pebbles and larger fragments are swiftly moving water and ice. Till and tillite are mixed aggregates, not included within the customary meanings of gravel and conglomerate. With these exceptions, all coarse transported clastics are accumulated either by wave action or by powerful currents of water. The effects of violent handling are evident in the rounding, just described, and in the preponderance of durable constituents. Survival on a beach exposed to vigorous wave attack or in the channel of a torrential stream depends on the relative hardness and toughness of the fragments. Unless the wave attack or the river journey has been short, all the soft and friable material will have been destroyed.

Quartz is far more common than any other mineral in the gravels and conglomerates, partly because of its superior resistance to abrasion, and partly because in many regions it is the only mineral occurring in large enough masses to supply fragments of pebble size. Most quartz pebbles are derived from quartz veins, pegmatite, or from an earlier pebble deposit. Quartz liberated by the weathering of granite is set free as sand size particles. Feldspar pebbles are scarce except in the arkosic sediments which are described on p. 166.

Of all rocks, the quartzites, both sedimentary and metamorphic, are easily the most durable. Hence quartzite appears in the gravels wherever it is available. If it is mixed with other rocks and subject to continued wear, the relative amount of quartzite increases through the gradual failure of weaker rocks. The preponderance of quartz in most sands is explained by the same principle of selective abrasion. Other rocks able to withstand the action of waves and swift rivers are: granite, granitic gneiss, dolerite, and locally, other hypabyssal rocks. In general, extrusive igneous rocks are weaker. Some hornblende schists are tough, but most of the other schists and slate break easily along the planes of foliation. The only resistant sedimentary rocks, apart from quartzite, are firmly cemented sandstones, and, more rarely, a compact and tightly indurated silty shale.

The description of a gravel or conglomerate requires an account of the lithology of the component fragments. In statistical studies, a **pebble count** includes the different amounts of contributing fragments, together with their shapes and sizes. To be used in investigations of geomorphology and stratigraphy, the pebble counts must follow a standard procedure of sampling and be made at localities appropriately spaced.

Occurrence

The study of gravel is simplified by its coarse texture and its usually obvious place in either the present cycle of erosion or in one recently ended. Coarse texture also facilitates the identification of the fragments and cement in a conglomerate, but these alone seldom contribute enough information to reveal the provenance of a conglomerate deposited during an earlier geologic time. The genesis of a coarse-textured, transported rock is determined largely by stratigraphic and structural criteria. Petrographic description is essential, but petrology plays a secondary role.

Gravel is laid down by streams and meltwater, it accumulates as beaches and other shore forms, and it is distributed as a sea-floor or lake-bottom deposit. Till is released from either moving or stagnant glaciers. The principal gravel deposits are arranged in the following list according to the media that transport and deposit them; it is a list of landforms where gravel may be conspicuous; it is not a petrographic classification.

Streams	Meltwater
Alluvial fans	Outwash
Pediment veneers	Kames
Channel deposits	Kame terraces
Scrolls, flood plains	Eskers
Deltas	
Waves and Currents	Glaciers
Beaches, beach plains	Ground, terminal, and
Bars, embankments	recessional moraines
Submarine talus	

The transporting power of streams in flood and the energy of storm waves are both so great that no dimensions can be set for the maximum size of boulders. The velocity of a stream is related directly to its discharge, and wave action is dependent upon the wind. Since the moving power of water is controlled by these fluctuating variables, most stream and shore gravels are poorly sorted, and their textures tend to vary both vertically and laterally. Exceptions are usually confined to deposits of small extent: crescent beaches below the cliffs of an exposed coast may consist entirely of cobbles or of flat rounded pebbles where the cliff is shale and the waves less powerful; a single flood plain scroll may be homogeneous. In general, however, the texture of gravel is mixed, and deposits of similar origin often show little resemblance. A common texture pattern is one that consists of two conspicuously contrasted sizes, particularly a mixture of pebbles and coarse sand. One explanation of this arrangement lies in the size of the openings between the larger fragments; they are large enough to trap and hold the sand grains, but the intermediate sizes and the suspended particles are swept along by the current.

Fossils in conglomerate are exceedingly rare, for abrasion destroys organic structures as it does any nonresistant matter. The remains of organisms are limited to thick-shelled marine invertebrates in rocks that are coarse sand rather than true gravels, to the bones of large vertebrates, and to fossils that were silicified during a previous cycle and have survived the later reworking.

With the exception of fragmental limestones, which constitute a special case, the only waterlaid conglomerates with a wide horizontal extent are **basal conglomerates.** These, as the term is generally understood, are mixtures of coarse sand with some gravel, formed by the encroachment of the sea. They represent the progressive advance of the shore and near-shore zone across the land. Locally, the basal member of a marine series may include a pebble-rich facies, but mostly they are sandstones rather than conglomerates.

Only under particular circumstances, such as the presence of distinctive fossils, is it possible to relate a conglomerate to its mode of origin from laboratory studies. Otherwise it must be examined in the field and seen in its stratigraphic relationships to other rocks.

Till

Till, and its lithified form, *tillite,* are the most hetrogeneous of all rocks. The transporting power of moving ice is not dependent upon velocity, so that boulders of any size can be carried, and with the boulders there may be mixed any, or all, of the finer grades. Usually the largest fraction consists of clay-size particles. **Boulder clay** refers to the common mixture in which these two extremes predominate. The materials included in till are limited only by the number of different rock types that occur along the course of the glacier, however most of the material that can be identified has been gathered within a few miles of the place where it is deposited. Scratched and faceted rocks are by no means common, but when present they are a sure guide to the origin of the deposit. Most fragments show no signs of modification by glacial transport, but are variously angular or rounded, depending upon their previous shape and the manner by which they were added to the glacier's load. Among Pleistocene tills, some are loose, others have been overridden by thick ice sheets and compacted by the pressure so that they are not easily loosened with a pick, and a few have been cemented.

Lithification and Color

The processes that bring about lithification are essentially similar for the conglomerates and sandstones. So also are the factors that determine color. The induration and colors of conglomerate are therefore included with the descriptions of sandstone on pp. 162 and 169.

SAND, SILT, AND SANDSTONE

Sand is a loose, clastic, deposit consisting principally of visible particles that are less than two millimeters in diameter. When lithified it is *sandstone*. Silt is included with sand in the present discussion because it is similar in mineralogy, and with allowance for its finer size, similar in history. **Siltstone** is an entirely valid term, but rocks to which it might be applied are usually known by other names.

Sands and silts are carried by either air or water. They are deposited wherever the current is no longer able to keep them in motion, but may resume their journey if the current freshens or if a change of conditions delivers them for transport by another medium. Thus sands on beaches and deserts are exposed to the moving power of both wind and water. Sand grains come to rest finally only at the bottom of a sea or lake beyond the reach of waves and currents, or when covered by later deposits, or when bound by lithification. The mobility of sand grains differs in kind and degree from that of other clastic materials. Clay is carried by weaker currents, but settles to the bottom slowly. When water-borne clay is exposed to the air it may be quickly anchored by vegetation in a moist climate, or dehydrated to firmness in a dry one. Gravels on the other hand are immune to wind transport and are moved only by swift water or ice.

For several reasons the sands and sandstones have been studied in greater detail than any of the other clastic rocks. Sand is used directly for many purposes, including building, abrasives, glass making, metal casting, and it is of particular importance in petroleum geology as a reservoir rock and for the migration of oil. The dimensions of its components facilitate their identification and, except for firmly bound sandstones, the grains are readily separated into their various grade sizes. From the analysis of grain size, grain shape, and mineralogy there have gradually evolved criteria for determining origin and techniques used in correlation.* Shales are too fine grained and too easily modified to lend themselves to these methods of study. If, however, a shale contains a sandstone member or a sandy facies, the interpretation of this coarser material may provide the clues necessary for the understanding of the associated sediments.

Composition

Quartz is so prevalent in sands and sandstones that these names have come to signify the quartzose varieties unless some qualifying term is added. Pure quartz sands and sandstones are nevertheless rare. The minerals most commonly associated with quartz are: chalcedony, potash-feldspar, muscovite, hornblende, magnetite, and garnet. If the last two minerals are abundant enough to be conspicuous, the rocks are named *magnetite sand* and *garnetiferous sand.* The minerals in question may be disseminated through the deposit, or concentrated into homogeneous lenses by gravity separation. If the amount of feldspar approaches or exceeds that of quartz, the sand is *feldspathic,* but the density difference between quartz and feldspar is insufficient to bring about their separation by natural sorting methods. Quartz-free sands of a single composition occur

* Students of sedimentation apply statistical methods to the distribution of grade sizes to determine the origin of sands. Correlations are based on the relative frequencies of persistent rare minerals, such as tourmaline and epidote. The procedures are specialized beyond the scope of this book.

locally where erosion is destroying a monomineralic rock. The calcite beach sands of Florida and the gypsum sand dunes of California are striking examples.

The grain size of sand limits the lithic fragments to particles of fine-textured rocks such as slate, phyllite, and firm shale.

Sand deposited in water may be mixed with simultaneously deposited chemical precipitates and organic substances; many sandstones contain introduced cementing materials.

Grain Size and Shape

Unless a sand has been sieved for the accurate measurement of its particles, the grain size can be approximately described as coarse, medium, or fine. Mixtures may include these sizes and also either pebbles or still finer grades. Since there are no terms to designate specific mixtures, each must be described, and the phrases used should indicate the relative degree of accuracy or approximation. Hypothetical examples are: "coarse sand with from 15 to 20 per cent of pebbles up to 8 mm in diameter," and "medium grained sand with an undetermined amount of fine sand and silt."

Sand grains carried by wind attain a higher degree of rounding than is achieved by abrasion in water, presumably because of the lower viscosity of air and the absence of a protecting water film. Otherwise roundness is a function of the hardness of the particles and the frequency and violence of contact. In either medium, the larger sizes tend to be more rounded, and silt fragments are prevailingly angular. Diagenesis may subsequently change the shapes of grains by either the addition or substraction of mineral matter (p. 163).

Lithification

The lithification of gravel, sand, and silt may be accomplished by the introduction of mineral matter that serves to cement the particles or by changes that take place within substances already present. Cementing material may enter by several methods. Water passing through the openings between grains may precipitate minerals from solution or may deposit colloidal matter that subsequently hardens. Ions may migrate into a rock permeated with water without the assistance of circulating solutions; the transfer is effected through the diffusion of ions. The most common introduced cements are carbonates, chiefly calcite, oxides of iron, and the silica minerals. Many rocks that appear to be cemented by limonite or hematite are actually bound by other substances, with enough iron oxide to impart the characteristic red or brown colors. The first stage in the cementing process is the deposition of a film of the introduced substance on the grain surfaces (Figure 22). If the action

 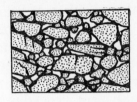 

FIGURE 22. **Left,** pebble coated with a thin layer of calcite which serves to attach smaller fragments; an early stage in the cementing process. **Center,** cross section through accumulation of clastic fragments (stippled), surrounded by introduced cement (black). The porosity is suggested by the remaining space (white). **Right,** quartz fragment outlined by a ferruginous surface film. Later quartz, added in crystallographic continuation with original grain, has developed crystal form.

is then discontinued, the particles are attached only at their points of contact, and the rock is friable and retains most of its original porosity. With continued deposition of cement, the pore spaces may be so filled that no megascopically visible openings remain.

Introduced silica may join crystallographically with the clastic grains of quartz and so increase their dimensions. Not infrequently the added quartz is terminated by crystal faces, thus transforming a more or less rounded grain to an angular crystal (Figure 22). Similar secondary growth has been recorded for many other minerals in sediments, but quartz is the only mineral commonly affected. A quartzose rock, cemented by quartz or chalcedony (or sometimes by opal) is a *quartzite*. Unless the meaning has been made entirely clear by the context, such a rock should be described as a *quartzite sandstone, quartzite conglomerate,* or *sedimentary quartzite,* to distinguish it from quartzites of metamorphic origin.

163

Induration also results from chemical and physical adjustments of components deposited contemporaneously with the clastic fragments. Binding materials derived from the original material of a sediment are referred to as *authigenic* to distinguish them from the *allogenic* (introduced) cements. Finely divided calcite sets as a firm paste, and, under pressure, changes to a crystalline aggregate. Also calcium carbonate from shells may be distributed between the clastic grains. In quartzose rocks that contain no obvious source of carbonate, it is impossible to distinguish between allogenic and authigenic calcite. When water is lost through evaporation, squeezing, or a slight temperature rise, the colloids stiffen, and with further loss of water, crystallize. Pressure and moderate heat also remove the water adsorbed by some of the clay minerals and ultimately bring about recrystallization. They are made over either to micaceous or chloritic substances, depending upon the available chemical ingredients.

Even though it may not be apparent whether the substances that make a rock cohere are original or introduced, their identification usually is not difficult. Calcite effervesces under a drop of cold, dilute acid, other carbonates effervesce when the rock is scratched to yield a fine powder. The iron oxides dissolve readily in warm hydrochloric acid. Silica cements are hard and impervious to acid. Also they may be recognized when the rock is broken, since a fracture passes alike through cement and fragments. In rocks bound otherwise, the break passes between the grains, leaving a sandy or pebbly surface. This test is useful to distinguish between the iron oxide cements and the dark red and brown jaspers that frequently resemble them. Unless recrystallization has proceeded too far, a bond derived from clay exudes an argillaceous odor from a freshly broken surface. Chlorite is recognized by its characteristic green; when present in fair abundance it is seldom masked completely by the other constituents.

Distribution

The more extensive deposits of sand and silt are listed below according to the different media by which they are distributed.

Sedimentary Rocks

Inclusion of all the known types of sand or of all the possible modes of occurrence would require an extended list, and no single classification can expect equally to meet the requirements of specialized studies in sedimentation, stratigraphy, economic geology, and other investigations where sands and sandstones are important. The grouping above is one of convenience to include the sands being distributed under the present cycle of erosion or in the recent past. Under the principle of uniformitarianism, it should embrace the sandstones of earlier geologic times.

Marine and Lacustrine Sands

The sands of seas and lakes consist of materials eroded at the shore and particles delivered from the land by rivers, wind, and, locally, by glaciers. The marine sands of the continental shelf and epeiric seas are the most extensive of all sandstone formations; they may begin at a beach and spread as far out as the currents can transport the sand, and the sand deposited by an encroaching sea extends as far as the sea transgresses.

Quartz is the predominant mineral. A sandstone may consist of clastic grains alone or, apart from introduced cements, may be mixed with a variety of precipitated material of either organic or inorganic origin. Many marine limestones contain contemporaneous calcite; when this mineral exceeds the clastic fraction, the rock is an *arenaceous limestone* rather than a *calcareous sandstone*. With increasing additions of the clay minerals the rocks grade from *argillaceous sandstone* to arenaceous clay rocks. These mixtures may also contain carbonates. **Greensand** owes its name and appearance to glauconite, a mineral that is abundant only in marine deposits where it occurs most commonly as rounded grains. Until recently it was generally believed that all glauconite is formed by direct

165

precipitation from sea water; however evidence has been produced to show that glauconite may also result from the alteration of biotite.

Few general statements apply to texture, as both grain size and the degree of rounding are variable. At a given shore locality, the largest grains are found on the beach and decrease in size away from the land; however coarse sands and gravels are known to occur in deep water, far from the shore. Formations described as basal conglomerates (p. 159) consist mostly of sand. Rounding is developed best in dune sands that have been reworked and redeposited by the waves of an advancing shore.

Fossils are fairly common in marine sandstones, particularly the remains of shells, but carbonaceous matter is abundant only if the sand is mixed with a large quantity of clay. Without stratigraphic evidence, marine fossils and abundant glauconite are the only reliable criteria for marine origin.

Fluvial Deposits

In a stable landscape, the burden transported and deposited by the river systems consists mostly of silt and clay-size particles. Coarse material is handled in large quantity only by swift streams: by headwater tributaries in steep country, by rivers as yet ungraded, and in time of flood. Alluvial fans, coarse channel gravels, and deltas of cobbles and pebbles in the lakes of high country are typical deposits. The most extensive accumulations laid down by rivers that flow to the sea are floodplains and deltas. Since grade size normally decreases toward the mouth of a river, the flood plains and deltas consist of fine sand, silt, and clay. In unconsolidated form, any mixtures of these particles are usually designated as clay, unless carefully examined, because their bulk appearance is that of clay, and organic matter is often present to darken and obscure the other components of the mixture. The common lithified rocks are argillaceous siltstones and sandstones, sandy and silty shales.

Arkose and Graywacke

Arkose and graywacke are distinctive varieties of sandstone. They are presumed to represent the depositional phases of cycles marked by diastrophic uplift. Arkose is distinguished from other sandstones by its large share of feldspar fragments, its angular grains, and poor sorting. The feldspar is mostly orthoclase and microcline, and may be either clean or weathered. Many feldspars are bounded by cleavage surfaces, as though they had been broken in transit. The other minerals are quartz and muscovite. The quartz is usually better rounded than the feldspar, and the muscovite occurs as flakes.

The texture of many arkosic rocks places them near the border-line between sandstone and conglomerate; if particles larger than two millimeters predominate, they are appropriately described as *arkosic conglomerate*. It is impossible to distinguish megascopically between quartz and feldspar in rocks made up of fine sand or silt, nevertheless a fine-textured arkose can often be identified by the characteristic glitter of muscovite flakes.

The grains may be held together by several substances, loosely by clay, more firmly by clay that has recrystallized, and many of the coarser rocks are cemented by silica. Many arkoses are colored red or brown by relatively small quantities of iron oxide mixed with the cementing medium. Although these "brownstones" were formerly much in demand for building, their subsequent disintegration by peeling and flaking shows that much of the rock so used was too porous for the purpose.

The mineralogy of arkose clearly indicates its derivation from either granite or granitic gneiss. The coarse texture, angularity, and the unaltered feldspar point to a relative short transport by swift streams. Further interpretation, based on field studies, leads to the conclusion that most arkose is laid down in regions of inland drainage, close to areas that are undergoing rapid uplift.

Graywackes are dark sandstones or siltstones, characteristic of Paleozoic and earlier geologic time. In the sandstones, the particles are chiefly quartz, with or without feldspar, but with few other minerals. Graywacke may also contain fragments of slate, phyllite, or other dark, fine-textured rocks. The silt particles of the finer graywackes are almost entirely quartz. The fragments are almost invariably angular, so that broken surfaces and edges feel rough. Graywacke is firm and tough because the particles are held in a compact matrix. This consists of minerals recrystallized from the

167

original intermixed clay rather than introduced cements. It pervades the rock so intimately that only the larger mineral fragments can be identified. Graywacke owes its dark green and dark gray colors to finely divided chlorite and carbonaceous matter. In hand specimens it is recognized only by its combination of sand texture, dark color, and difficult, irregular fracture.

Graywacke is interpreted as the product of the rapid erosion of a rising area of metamorphic and sedimentary rocks. Many graywackes were deposited as deltas and grade laterally into marine formations.

Outwash

Typical glacial outwash deposits grade from mixtures of sand and gravel near the source to silt and sand at the outer edge. The sorting is irregular, the shapes and composition of the sand are mixed, and it is devoid of petrographic characteristics that might serve to distinguish it from other water-laid detritus. Outwash deposits are commercially important in many localities as sources of sand and gravel.

Eolian Deposits

Wind blown sands are confined largely to desert and semi-desert regions and to narrow belts along the shores of lakes and seas. They differ from other sands principally in their more uniform sorting and more complete rounding. Apart from typical eolian cross bedding, these are the characteristics used to distinguish eolian sandstones from water-laid formations. Quartz grains, long carried by the wind, acquire peculiar "frosted" surfaces. Under the microscope this is seen to consist of a close pattern of tiny angular pits, each the result of a collision violent enough to chip the surface. Desert sands often approach a monomineralic composition; dunes along the shore tend to be more heterogeneous.

Loess is a wind deposit of silt with more or less clay. The particles are angular fragments of quartz, feldspar, and mica. The typical grayish tan color is produced by a small quantity of iron oxide. Modern loess is neither cemented nor compact; nevertheless it possesses enough strength to cohere and retain vertical walls. This appears to result from the solution and redeposition of gypsum or of the other relatively soluble substances that are found near the surface in arid regions. In the loess of northern China these salts are deposited in vertical tubes that mark the positions of grass roots. Since stratification is absent, this is the only structure to be expected in loess.

Colors of Sandstone and Conglomerate

The colors of clastic sedimentary rocks depend upon only a few basic factors, and these account for the colors of nearly all rocks of other categories:

1. Rock-forming minerals that are free from iron and free from compounds of certain other less common elements, such as copper and manganese, are either white or colorless and clear.
2. A few minerals, notably pink or red potash feldspar and amethyst, are characteristically colored by minute quantities of an impurity.
3. Solid inclusions, scattered through a normally light-colored mineral, may darken the entire mineral.
4. Compounds that include ferrous iron are either green (olivine, chlorite), brown (siderite), or black (ilmenite). The color deepens with increasing iron content.
5. Limonite and hematite produce different shades of yellow, tan, brown, orange, light or dark red, depending upon the amount of iron oxide and whether one or both compounds are present.
6. Graphite and carbonaceous substances are black.

The color displayed by a rock as a unit is the result produced by the colors of its various components. It depends partly on the absolute amount of coloring matter or colored minerals, but more on the manner in which these are distributed through the rock. A relatively small quantity of a strong coloring agent (the iron oxides and carbon), if finely divided, is often sufficient to determine the color of the entire mass.

Pure quartz sand is white, but the bulk colors of most sands are either gray from the mixed-in dark grains, or tan from stains and coatings of iron oxide, or, more commonly, intermediate between gray and tan. Similarly, the general color effect produced by a gravel, or any uncemented mixed aggregate, is the blended result of the colors of its components. A cementing substance may either modify the color of the fragments or obscure it entirely. Calcite cement is nearly always white, silica cements may also be white, but many of them are yellow, red, or brown jaspers. Red and dark brown sandstones and conglomerates are not necessarily cemented by hematite or limonite; these deep colors may result from a very small iron content distributed as fine particles through some other cementing medium. An equal quantity of iron in the form of magnetite would produce almost no color change in a quartz sand. A similar red or rusty appearance may be caused by oxidation, and it is necessary to distinguish actual rock colors from colors resulting from weathering. Unless clastic rocks contain clay, they are seldom darkened by carbonaceous matter.

CLAYS AND SHALES

The term *clay* is used with two distinct meanings; to describe aggregates composed largely of the clay minerals and to designate those consisting of fine particles. This leads to ambiguity, for although the clay minerals are always excessively fine, any rock material may have a clay texture if it is sufficiently comminuted. Confusion can be avoided by using *pelite* or *lutite* for the grade size, and *argillaceous* for composition, wherever the context does not make clear which meaning of clay is intended.

Properties

Although there are several different clay minerals, all of them are essentially hydrated aluminum silicates, formed by the weathering or other alteration of the feldspars and many other minerals of similar composition. Feldspar is the chief source because of its preponderance in the lithosphere; clay is consequently the most abundant product of the chemical destruction of rocks. Clay-size particles, other than the clay minerals, include volcanic dust, organic substances, and rocks ground to powder by abrasion.

Many clays are plastic when wet. This property is usually ascribed to the presence of substances in colloidal suspension. Colloidal particles are the smallest that can still be defined as solids. Those in a clay complex include the colloids released by weathering, also organic colloids, and the products of extreme comminution.

Transported clays and the resulting clay rocks appear homogeneous when they contain no megascopically visible components. Actually most of them are mixtures, both in the mechanical sense, and in composition. If they contain even a small fraction of silt or sand, these coarser particles are easily detected, because they destroy the feeling of complete smoothness that characterizes a clay or shale that is free from grit. The size and quantity of the coarse fraction can be determined in loose material by washing away the clay and sieving the remainder.

Pure clays and some shales are white, but these are exceptional. Most of the transported deposits are colored by iron compounds, organic matter, or both. Carbonaceous matter is present in nearly all shales, darkening them to gray or black. Shades of green and blue result from ferrous compounds, and the yellows, reds, and browns betray the presence of iron oxides.

With the addition of calcite, a shale becomes *calcareous,* with quartzose sand grains, it is described as *arenaceous.* With increasing amounts of these substances the rocks grade into argillaceous limestones and sandstones. Rocks with these mixed compositions are common, and it is often difficult to decide in which category a given specimen should be placed.

Induration

Argillaceous deposits can be found in any stage of lithification from loose clay to firm shale. A distinction can be made between them by assigning to shale those rocks that fail to soften when soaked in water. The hardening of clay takes place through several processes. Under mild pressure most of the water is squeezed out, and the particles are brought into close contact and tend to cohere. The familiar example of clay soils baked to firmness under a summer sun indicates that heat is an effective agent; the accompanying mud cracks show that it is a dehydrating process. Another method of hardening takes place through the "setting" of colloids. It is probable that both heat and pressure contribute to this process, partly by removing the excess water and partly by promoting the subsequent crystallization. **Argillite** is a particularly hard shale, high in silica, and presumably held together by silica minerals that were formerly in a colloidal state. Since clays are relatively impervious, there is little or no cementing by introduced mineral matter.

When clays are buried beneath younger sediments, they are necessarily subjected to vertical pressure, with a magnitude proportional to the thickness of the overlying strata. In addition to the resulting compaction and dehydration, the pressure also brings about recrystallization. Clay minerals are particularly affected because they are formed at the surface of the earth, and in general are stable only under surface conditions. As a result, micaceous and chloritic minerals are formed. These are flaky in habit and develop with their larger dimensions perpendicular to the pressure, and consequently parallel to the bedding. The change is probably assisted by the flaky habit of most of the clay minerals and the tendency for flakes to settle flat side down. This partial recrystallization within a shale is analogous to the development of foliation in a slate, but takes place in a much milder degree. Many shales are **fissile**, that is, they tend to split parallel to the bedding. This structure may be even and parallel, or highly irregular; the surfaces may be either smooth or rough. It is not possible to determine megascopically whether the structure is a secondary one, brought about by recrystallization, or a primary arrangement produced by interruptions or changes during deposition.

Occurrence

Coarse fragments come to rest almost instantly wherever the velocity of water falls below the point necessary to keep them moving. Clay particles, on the contrary, are carried in suspension; they are transported by the weakest currents, and even in an environment of dead calm they settle to the bottom slowly. Some clays seem to remain suspended indefinitely; the fine particles may carry electric charges of like sign that are strong enough to keep them apart by their mutual repulsion. These forces vanish in the presence of electrolytes. Thus when sea water mingles with fresh water at the mouth of a river, the charges are neutralized. The particles are then free to settle. Often they cohere, and the resulting aggregates grow until gravity pulls them to the bottom.

Typical clay deposits are laid down in places that mark the end of effective transport for any material not carried in solution. The floors of lakes, seas, and ocean, the flood plains, and deltas are the common examples. It is doubtful if any shales yet found on the continents have been derived from clay originally deposited on the deep ocean floor,* so the deposits that make up the bulk of argillaceous material on the lands are:

1. Marine deposits of the continental (epeiric and epicontinental) seas.
2. Lacustrine (lake) deposits.
3. Fluviatile (river) deposits, principally flood plains and deltas.

Most marine shales are neutral in color, from gray to black, although some are distinctly green from glauconite or other ferrous iron compounds. Their compositions and textures are frequently mixed. Qualifying terms such as *carbonaceous, calcareous, silty,* and *arenaceous* indicate appreciable amounts of nonargillaceous or coarser material. The marine origin of a shale can be determined only through its field relations or by marine fossils.

Lake clays and shales are usually marked by even bedding. Although they may be dark, or strongly colored, lacustrine deposits often include light colored or even white layers. Many lake clays consist of a succession of laminas, thin and even layers. Sometimes these occur in obvious alternate arrangement, strongly marked by differences in color, composition, or texture. Others consist of similar layers, but with each showing the same vertical gradation in physical properties or composition. When it can be shown that the clay was deposited in a lake adjacent to melting ice, the pairs of alternating layers, or the layers with gradational properties, are interpreted as *varves.* Varves are annual layers, analogous to the rings of annual growth in trees. The differences within a varve are correlated with the cycle of the seasons, one set of properties correspond-

* Devices for obtaining core samples from the ocean floor have been used for several years and are being improved rapidly. Through these instruments and others, geologic studies of the ocean are being steadily extended, and information is accumulating from depths that have been inaccessible until now.

ing to summer, another to winter, or with a seasonal change from wet to drier conditions. However, not all alternating or uniformly grading laminas are varves. They may result from any cause that occasionally interrupts deposition or brings about a change in local conditions.

Flood plain deposits normally contain a large amount of silt. Their stratification may be fairly even, but in general the bedding planes are less conspicuous than in sediments that were spread out in lakes and seas. Other differences result from their exposed position on the land. Where oxidizing conditions prevail, the flood plain sediments may be red or brown; deposits laid down in swamps and marshes are richly mixed with organic matter and consequently dark or black. Sufficient concentrations of preserved vegetable matter may interrupt the clastic sediments with layers of peat or coal. Except in swamps, there are few opportunities on a flood plain for organisms to be buried and preserved, so that fossils are far less common than in sediments deposited below water. Favorable conditions for mud cracks occur wherever the surface is covered by occasional and temporary sheets of water.

The typical deltaic formations are those deposited by large and mature rivers. These sediments merge upstream with flood plain deposits and grade seaward into marine formations. They can be distinguished only by their field relations, particularly by the typical delta cross bedding. Like the flood plain sediments, such deltas rarely consist of clay particles alone, but usually contain much silt. Graywacke is the common rock of the ancient (Paleozoic and older) deltas.

SEDIMENTARY ROCKS FORMED BY CHEMICAL PROCESSES

Even though the distinction between chemical and physical processes is not always clear,* it affords a convenient method for dividing most sedimentary rocks into two contrasting groups, according to origin. Since many rocks are mixtures, with constituents accumulated by both sets of processes, it is frequently difficult to determine

---

* For instance, when a solid is precipitated by the evaporation of its solvent, the change, though apparently simple, is actually a complex transformation that can be described only under the laws of physical chemistry. Few changes, in which solutions play a part, can be made to fit into a simple scheme that attempts to label some effects "physical" and others "chemical."

which has played the major role. Included in the substances of chemical origin are the remains of organisms (shells, bones, vegetation, etc.), precipitates formed indirectly through the activity of organisms, products of inorganic reactions, and minerals formed by the evaporation of water. There are some nonclastic sedimentary rocks with origins not yet explained and others that have been formed by the replacement of earlier rocks.

The composition of a rock is not always a guide to its origin; limestone can be formed in several different ways and, once formed, may undergo various transformations that may conceal its earlier history. For this reason it is not practicable to group the chemically formed rocks by origin alone. In the following list they are arranged partly by composition and partly by origin:

> Limestone and dolomitic limestone
> Silicious rocks
> Iron ores and ferruginous sediments
> Salt, gypsum, anhydrite
> Peat and coal

LIMESTONES

The term "limestone" brings to mind no set of related visible properties such as are evoked by the names of basalt, obsidian, or shale. The only attribute that all limestones hold in common is that they consist essentially of calcium carbonate. Otherwise they differ widely in texture, color, content and structure, in origin, and even in their association with other sedimentary rocks. Their diversity results partly from original differences and partly from the peculiar physical and chemical properties of calcite, for this mineral is much more susceptible to recrystallization, to solution, and to replacement, than any other common rock-forming mineral. Consequently, when the conditions that surround a limestone are changed, diagenetic processes may bring about a complete reorganization of the rock.

Origin

Although limestone may locally form in lakes and even in rivers, the extensive formations are all marine. After a limestone has been formed it may be modified in many ways by mechanical and chemical changes, but the primary process of deposition always involves the extraction of calcium carbonate from water. The original precipitate may include aragonite, but since this is the less stable form, it is eventually converted to calcite. Most limestones are formed directly by organic processes and consist largely of organic remains. These may be corals, other coral reef organisms, molluscs, other "shells" and their megascopic fragments, and microscopic material, including smaller fragments and the tests of foraminifera.

Appreciable quantities of calcium carbonate can be held in solution only in the presence of carbon dioxide. When this substance is reduced below the necessary concentration, calcium carbonate separates as a fine white precipitate:

$$Ca(HCO_3)_2 \rightarrow CO_2 + H_2O + \underline{CaCO_3}$$

The reaction can be brought about by any process capable of removing sufficient carbon dioxide. It takes place through the activity of some algae that extract carbon dioxide for their own use and also when relatively cold waters enter warm latitudes and the rise of temperature expels a part of the dissolved gas. Both processes form limestone indirectly, the first by organic, and the second by inorganic change. However, the amount of limestone made by these methods is unknown, for it is not possible to determine the origin of a fine-grained limestone unless it contains structures that reveal the way it was formed.

Varieties

Coquina is a limestone of comparatively recent origin, consisting of shell fragments and shells. It is porous and only partly cemented. Compacted rocks with abundant shell material are *shell* limestones. They may be described more specifically as *coral, crinoidal,* or *cryptozoan* limestones if one group of these organisms predominates. *Chalk* is a fine-grained, generally loose, white rock, made up largely of the remains of foraminifera. Lithographic limestone is compact, homogeneous, and so fine-grained that it was used for the printing process from which it takes its name. *Travertine* is a land deposit, usually formed in caves as dripstone. It is a secondary rock in the sense that the calcite was dissolved from another limestone, or calcareous rock, and reprecipitated. Stalactites and stalagmites are usually crystalline and irregularly banded. *Tufa* is porous, spongy material, deposited by springs and sometimes along the course of a river. It may be penetrated by tubular holes that mark the positions of twigs upon which it had gathered. Both travertine and tufa are precipitated inorganically from water supersaturated with calcium carbonate.

Although the actual precipitation of calcite takes place chemically, many limestones consist either wholly or partly of fragments. These are **clastic** limestones. Coquina and most shell limestones contain enough broken shells to be placed in this category, and pieces of corals and coral rocks are often abraded as though by wave erosion. Limestone intraformational breccia is also a clastic rock, with limestone fragments embedded in a matrix of the same material. Their structure appears to result from the breaking up of a hardened crust and a subsequent mixing of the pieces with the underlying softer substance. Usually the clastic habit of fragmental limestones can be seen to advantage only on a weathered surface, since exposure etches the cementing calcite so that the fragments stand out in low relief.

Oolitic limestone resembles moderately coarse sandstone and displays similar structures, particularly cross bedding. Oolites have been observed forming in different ways. Commonly they consist of concentric layers of calcite surrounding a silt-size quartz grain. A rock consisting of these is interpreted as a shallow water deposit. The nucleus, agitated by waves or currents, is rolled about the bottom, and grows by the accretion of calcite that sticks to the surface.

LIMESTONES MODIFIED BY DIAGENESIS

Crystalline Limestone

When pressure is applied to finely divided calcite, the minute particles tend to coalesce and ultimately unite to form visible crystals. Although this recrystallization can take place in a dry state, it seems more than likely that it can also be brought about by solution and reprecipitation, without the influence of pressure. In some rocks the process is localized and produces isolated calcite crystals a millimeter or so in diameter, scattered through an aphanitic ground mass. Other limestones recrystallize evenly throughout the rock to a finely granular but recognizably crystalline texture. Continuation of the process leads to the coarser mosaic of calcite crystals that is identified with marble. In the progressive recrystallization there is no point that can be taken to mark the division between crystalline limestone and marble; however a rock can be safely left in the former category if it has not been deformed, or if no typical metamorphic minerals have developed, or if the associated sedimentary rocks are free from metamorphic changes.

Dolomitic Limestone

Dolomitic limestones are those in which the essential mineral is dolomite rather than calcite. Rocks of intermediate composition are called *magnesian* limestone. Dolomitic rocks are easily identified in the laboratory by their failure to effervesce under acid except on freshly bruised or scratched surfaces. In the field many dolomites can be recognized by a slightly rusty appearance of the weathered outcrops. The carbonate compounds usually contain a small amount of ferrous iron which is changed to limonite by oxidation.

The origin of dolomitic limestones is obscure. Apparently, dolomite is precipitated directly only from warm and concentrated saline waters, and most dolomitic limestone is formed by replacement. Many and, perhaps, most of the limestones and marbles of the pre-Cambrian and early Paleozoic are dolomitic. Some of these are formations of extraordinary thickness, and if they are replacement products, the amount of introduced magnesium is so large that it is difficult to account for it. The only obvious source of large quantities of dissolved magnesium is sea water, which at the present time contains 0.14 per cent of this element.

Silicious Limestone

Silicious limestones are those that contain precipitated chalcedony. The term is not applied to limestone with detrital fragments of silicious minerals. The chalcedony occurs as concretions and replacements. The concretions tend to be rounded and nodular, with dark-colored *flint* in chalk beds and lighter-colored *chert* in other limestones. *Chert* is also used as the name for chalcedony replacements. When chalcedony is substituted for the carbonate minerals, the replacement is sometimes highly selective and sometimes without any apparent control; the silicifaction may be restricted to certain layers, or confined to fossils, or it may produce irregular masses that meet the host rock with intricately crenulated contacts. Quite often the metasomatism is so intimate that the chalcedony preserves the fine details of the former texture and retains the internal structures of fossils and oolites. When the replacement is carried to completion, an entire formation may be converted from limestone to chert.

SILICIOUS ROCKS

The only sedimentary rocks, made up of more or less uncontaminated silica and known to be laid down as primary deposits, are those consisting of organic remains and the local deposits of hot springs. **Diatomaceous earth** is a loose, extremely fine, white, powdery rock, somewhat resembling chalk. It is made up of the silicious parts of diatoms, microscopic, unicellular plants. Similarly, **radiolarian chert** consists of the silicious skeletons of radiolaria, which are microscopic unicellular animals. In hand specimens, a radiolarian chert is indistinguishable from cherts of other origins.

The remaining silicious rocks are either replacements, chert formations containing iron minerals, or other rocks of mixed composition.

IRON ORES AND IRON-RICH SEDIMENTS

Sedimentary rocks rich enough in iron minerals to be worked as ore are by no means common, but they are widely distributed, both in space and through the geologic column. Also, in several localities the stratigraphic section includes silicious and carbonate rocks with unusually high percentages of iron. The sedimentary ores and the "iron formations" have been studied in great detail, but their origins are still obscure. One reason for this is that the present cycle fails to exhibit the deposition of iron minerals in similar associations. The only sedimentary iron ore now being deposited is the limonite **bog iron** of the eastern Baltic region. It accumulates on the floors of shallow fresh water lakes as porous, spongy masses mixed with clay. It is attributed to the action of bacteria that precipitate ferric hydroxide from various soluble ferrous compounds. Since the older deposits are found chiefly in association with marine deposits, the bog iron is not interpreted as their modern counterpart.

The megascopic minerals of the sedimentary iron ores are hematite and siderite, but the deposits often include large quantities of the iron-rich chlorites (chamosite and greenalite). The bedded hematite deposits are commonly oolitic. Some of these are primary ores, deposited directly, but whether the hematite and the oolites are original or have acquired their present characteristics as a result of diagenesis is not always certain. Other oolitic hematite has been formed by the replacement of oolitic limestone by the infiltration of iron compounds. Siderite rarely occurs pure; it is mixed with silicious material or mingled with clay.

The typical iron formations are mixtures of the various sedimentary iron minerals with either chalcedony or quartz. The silica minerals may appear somewhat granular or may be excessively fine grained, but they are always deeply stained by iron compounds. Some of the rocks are sharply banded, with alternate layers of iron and silica minerals; others appear as homogeneous mixtures. By various methods of concentration, the iron formations of the Canadian Shield supplied the rich ore deposits of that region. They consist mainly of hematite, with local conversions to magnetite. These deposits, however, and the theories concerning their origin are matters that lie in the domain of economic geology and are not within the provenance of this book.

SALT, GYPSUM, AND ANHYDRITE

Wherever an enclosed body of water is continuously exposed to a sufficiently dry climate, salts may be precipitated by the evaporation of the water. The water may be an inland lake in desert country or an arm of the sea that has become detached from the ocean. If the salt deposits are to accumulate in appreciable thickness, it is necessary that the water supply be replenished, since the amount of solids that can be dissolved in a shallow lake or bay is limited by the depth of the water. It is also essential that there be no outlet by which the water can escape. These conditions are met in the Dead Sea and similar lakes, where the inflow of river water is in approximate balance with the water lost by evaporation. Analogous situations exist along arid coasts, where bays with narrow inlets receive a current of sea water flowing in to take the place of water that evaporates.

The ocean contains approximately three and a half pounds of dissolved solids in each hundred pounds of sea water; the **salinity** is three and a half per cent. Although traces of many chemical ele-

TABLE 18.   Salts in Sea Water

Ions		Compounds	
Na	30.592	NaCl	77.76
Mg	3.725	MgCl$_2$	10.88
Ca	1.197	MgSO$_4$	4.74
K	1.106	CaSO$_4$	3.60
		K$_2$SO$_4$	2.64
Cl	55.292	MgBr$_2$	.22
SO$_4$	7.692	CaCO$_3$	.34
CO$_3$	.207		
Br	.188		

Note: From F. W. Clarke, U.S.G.S. Bulletin 700.
Specific gravity of sea water, 1.027.
Specific gravity of oceanic salts, 2.25.
Salinity, 3.5 per cent.

ments can be detected in sea water, only a few substances are quantitatively important. These are shown in Table 18, as ions in the left-hand column and computed as salts on the right.

If sea water is evaporated in the laboratory, the various salts are precipitated in inverse order of their solubility, with the least soluble substance forming first as a layer at the bottom. The succeeding layers consist of the progressively more soluble compounds, with the most soluble at the top. The order is CaCO$_3$, gypsum, halite, double salts, including Mg, Cl, and SO$_4$, and finally, potassium compounds. Halite does not precipitate until only about one-tenth of the water remains. Few desert lakes approach the composition of sea water, and where sea water is evaporating, it may be contaminated by river water and other sources. Also the evaporation of sea water is seldom continued far enough to precipitate the salts of the later, more soluble fractions, and if these are deposited, they are easily redissolved and carried away. It is for these reasons that potash salts are so rare that they cannot be included among the common rocks. Layers of gypsum and salt, however, are known in many localities and are useful indicators of the climate under which they were deposited.

Gypsum may occur alone or be covered by salt. Together they suggest that they were formed either by the direct evaporation of sea water or in a lake that received its waters from a region of marine sedimentary rocks from which the sea salts have been removed during the course of erosion. Gypsum, not accompanied by salt, may be formed if evaporation has failed to precipitate the salt or if the salt has been deposited and then subsequently removed. Salt, without gypsum, cannot be formed directly from sea water. It may represent salt that has been dissolved from a gypsum-salt sequence and transported to another evaporation basin, or it may precipitate from water that has removed only the salt from the surrounding drainage area.

Gypsum changes readily to anhydrite ($CaSO_4$) with loss of water. This dehydration takes place at comparatively low temperatures, but the hydration of anhydrite is a slower and less common process. Experiments indicate that anhydrite can precipitate directly from *warm* saline water. Anhydrite is distinguished from gypsum by its higher specific gravity (2.9) and greater hardness. Both are white or light gray when pure, but are often contaminated. They may resemble limestone, but do not effervesce when treated with acid.

Several commercially important salts are not formed from sea water and occur only in the evaporation products of inland lakes. Among these are nitrates and the borates and carbonates of sodium.

PEAT AND COAL

Peat

Peat forms where vegetable matter accumulates in the stagnant water of swamps and bogs, an environment that presumes poor drainage and a moist climate. The essential process is an incomplete, arrested decomposition of the vegetation. Some of the bacteria that are the agents of these biochemical changes depend upon oxygen; as this element is used up their work is inhibited. Also some of the decomposition products are acid, which further interferes with bacterial action and prevents the complete destruction of the vegetation. Because there is no free circulation of water, the oxygen is not replenished nor is the acid removed. Hence the formation of peat may be regarded as a partial decay with a pickeling process added.

Peat is a fibrous, soft, spongy substance in which plant remains, particularly stems, can be recognized easily. The color varies from tan, through deeper shades of brown, to almost black. It is used as a fuel in some localities, but its heating value is low because of the high water content. When either peat or coal is burned, it leaves far more ash than does wood. Wood ashes contain only the mineral substances present in vegetation; most of the ash left by peat or coal comes from clay that became mixed with vegetation in the peat bog.

Lignite

Lignite, "brown coal," is more compact and darker than peat, and it contains less water. It is formed from peat by the vertical pressure of accumulating later sediments. Like peat, it is found in many places but is used only where more efficient fuels are not available. It may occur in other sedimentary rocks either as persistent beds or as thin streaks. Its chief interest in petrology is as the intermediate stage between peat and bituminous coal and as an indicator of the climate and topography required for its initial deposition.

Bituminous Coal

Bituminous coal, the coal of industry, is sometimes called "soft coal" to distinguish it from anthracite or "hard coal." Its physical properties and composition vary through the wide range that separates lignite from anthracite and also because of original differences in the vegetation. All of it is black, and most of it shows a banded structure, with the layers or laminas varying in luster from glossy to dull, from faintly granular to uniformly homogeneous. Many bituminous coals are separated by vertical fractures more or less at right angles, so that they break into crudely rectangular blocks. Some layers are firm and compact, others are soft enough to soil the fingers, and still others crumble to coarse granules. Authigenic pyrite occurs in some coal, otherwise no visible minerals are to be expected. The composition of coal is usually expressed by a **proximate analysis,** in which the constituents determined are: moisture, ash, volatile substances, and fixed carbon. The volatile ingredients are driven off as inflammable gases when coal is heated; the fixed carbon includes the compounds that burn directly as solids.

Anthracite

Anthracite is found only in folded strata; apparently the pressure that results solely from the weight of overlying rock is not enough to bring about the change from bituminous coal. Seams of coal that can be traced from folded to undisturbed rock invariably illustrate this principle. Anthracite is harder than bituminous coal, is homogeneous, has a bright rather than dull luster, and tends to break in curved or irregular fractures rather than into blocks. During the change from bituminous coal, both moisture and volatiles are lost, so that the *relative* amounts of fixed carbon and ash increase, while the total weight decreases.

If the conditions that govern folding are sufficiently intense to effect a low-grade metamorphism in the containing rocks, the carbon compounds may be converted to graphite. When this has taken place, the coal may consist entirely of ash and carbon and consequently will not ignite.

DENSITY AND POROSITY

On the average, the densities of sedimentary rocks are considerably lower than those of rocks formed in other ways. The explanation lies partly in the mineral composition of the sediments and partly in their porosity. The silica minerals (quartz, chalcedony, opal) and the various clay minerals are the chief contributors to sedimentary rocks, and all these are substances of low specific gravity. Coal, gypsum, and rock salt are even lighter materials. Calcite (2.72) is slightly heavier than the average granite (2.67) of Table 9 and almost equal in density to the average granodiorite. The only minerals heavier than calcite and significant in that they may be the only essential constituents in a sedimentary formation are dolomite, anhydrite, siderite, and the various iron oxides. All these together, however, provide only a small fraction of all sedimentary material.

The porosity of a rock is the per cent of pore space by volume. Among the common sedimentary rocks few are compact enough to be considered as essentially nonporous, although some shales and limestones may have porosities of less than one per cent. On the other hand, the porosity of a sandstone or shale may exceed thirty per cent. Several factors contribute to the wide range of variability. A rock may be highly porous because the pressure or the time that pressure was applied has been insufficient to bring about a more nearly complete compaction. In others, entering solutions may have failed to fill the openings with a cementing substance, or water may have enlarged the pore spaces by solution. Diagenesis, notably the dolomitization of limestone, may produce voids as a result of shrinkage.

Except for the relatively compact rocks, it is necessary to distinguish between the specific gravity of the solid components and the density of the rock as a whole. **Bulk density** is the density of a rock with the pore spaces computed as part of the total volume. The density of the rock with the spaces completely filled with water is the **wet bulk density.** For a given rock both of these values are necessarily lower than the specific gravity of its mineral components. An hypothetical example follows.

Assume a sandstone having a porosity of 20% and consisting only of quartz grains. Assume also a sample with a total volume of 100 cc.

1. The specific gravity of the mineral grains is that of quartz, 2.65.
2. The rock consists of 80 cc of quartz, 20 cc of voids.
3. The dry weight of the sample is therefore 80×2.65, or 212 g. The bulk density is then 2.12 g/cc.
4. Since 1 cc of water weighs 1 g, the total weight of the sample, with spaces filled with water, is $212 + 20$, or 232 g, and the wet bulk density is 2.32 g/cc.

CHEMICAL COMPOSITION OF THE SEDIMENTARY ROCKS

When sedimentary rocks are used in the chemical industries, such as the preparation of salt and the manufacture of cement and glass, the composition is of the utmost importance. But in geologic investigations that deal with sedimentary rocks as stratigraphic units or in studies of ecology or structure, it is seldom necessary to resort to chemical analysis. Because igneous rocks are classified by a scheme that is essentially chemical, analyses are needed for the precise identification of rocks that are excessively fine grained, or glassy, or profoundly altered. The chemical analysis of such rocks provides a reasonable guide to the minerals that are actually present, or that would have formed under different cooling conditions, or that existed before the alteration took place. On the other hand, the physical properties of most sedimentary rocks, especially the clastics, give a clearer picture of their origins than would be shown by an exact determination of the mineralogy. To this last generalization the clays and shales are notable exceptions, for clay minerals differ in origin and are not all derived from the same source materials. Consequently the identification of clay minerals has become increasingly important in many specialized studies undertaken during the past few years. However, the compositions of the various hydrated aluminum silicates that constitute the clay minerals are so similar that they are not differentiated by chemical analyses of the containing rocks. X-ray photographs and thermal analyses are the only reliable methods of identification.

Even though chemical analyses are seldom included in the descriptions of sedimentary rocks, a general knowledge of the distribution of their chemical constituents is useful. Chemical analyses serve to emphasize the similarity of a few sedimentary rocks to some igneous rocks and to point out the sharp differences of most. Also when a metamorphic rock of obscure but unmixed parentage is analyzed, its composition will usually indicate the rock from which it was derived.

The late Dr. F. W. Clarke of the U.S. Geological Survey combined the chemical analyses of many scores of sedimentary rocks and presented the results as composites of the three major types.

These are given in Table 19 with the minor constituents omitted. It is to be emphasized that these were prepared as *composite* analyses and not to represent the average compositions of the rocks.

It will be clear that silica is the predominant constituent of the sandstones and conglomerates and that in the more quartzose varieties of these rocks it will almost exclude the other oxides. With increasing amounts of alkali feldspar, as in arkose, the compositions approach those of the granites. Relatively pure limestones and dol-

TABLE 19. Composition of Sedimentary Rocks

	Sandstones	Shales	Limestones
SiO_2	78.66	58.38	5.19
Al_2O_3	4.78	15.47	0.81
Fe_2O_3	1.08	4.03	} 0.54
FeO	0.30	2.46	
MgO	1.17	2.45	7.90
CaO	5.52	3.12	42.61
Na_2O	0.45	1.31	0.05
K_2O	1.32	3.25	0.33
H_2O (total)	1.64	5.02	0.77
CO_2	5.04	2.64	41.58
Other	0.45	2.50	0.31

Note: From F W. Clarke, U.S.G.S. Bulletin 770.

omitic limestones approximate the composition of calcite and dolomite. In the shales the chief constituents are silica and alumina, the major components of the clay minerals and of other minerals derived from clay by diagenesis. However the amount of silica almost always exceeds the quantity required for the common aluminum silicates. This can be seen from the silica-alumina ratio of the minerals that are likely to occur in shales. The ratios given below are approximate and refer to weight and not to molecular proportions. Appreciable quantities of potash feldspar cannot be expected as an original constituent of argillaceous rocks, but this mineral is included for comparison.

	SiO_2	Al_2O_3
Kaolinite	1.2	1
Muscovite	1.2	1
Chlorite	2	1
Potash feldspar	3.6	1

The excess silica is partly accounted for by various other silicate minerals, but most of it occurs as "free" silica, in the form of colloidal silica, opal, chalcedony, or quartz. In practically all argillaceous rocks that contain the alkalies, potash exceeds soda. This is explained by the tendency of some clay minerals to adsorb potash, whereas the soda is removed in solution.

The interpretation of the mineral composition from the chemical analysis of a sedimentary rock is a useful exercise in understanding rock chemistry, even though it cannot lead to results that are either qualitatively or quantitatively accurate. Also it will show approximately the kinds of materials and the amounts that give a rock a mixed character, in contrast to hypothetically pure (quartzose) sandstone, limestone, or clay-shale. Thus the sandstone shown in Table 19 would be expected to contain carbonates of calcium and magnesium to make up slightly more than ten per cent of the rock. Since nearly all the iron is present in the ferric state, it could be safely interpreted as either hematite or limonite. Only if such an analysis were accompanied by an actual specimen would it be possible to tell whether the alkalies are present in feldspar, or held by clay minerals, or in the form of micaceous minerals of primary or secondary origin. The composite analysis of shale indicates a large but indeterminate quantity of free silica and somewhat more than five per cent of carbonates. The ferrous iron might be held either as a carbonate or united with other elements in silicate minerals. The analysis shows the expected excess of potash over soda. The hypothetical limestone in the same table is a somewhat magnesian rock, with only a small percentage of silicates, probably including some free silica and little else.

SUGGESTIONS FOR STUDY

1. For general purposes a loose sand can be examined conveniently by spreading a well-mixed sample thinly on squared millimeter paper. The white background facilitates identification of fragments and determination of their shapes. By manipulating a magnet below the paper, grains of magnetite can be drawn to one side. Interpolation between the ruled lines gives a sufficiently accurate measurement of grain size for particles with diameters of not less than 0.1 mm. It is strongly recom-

mended that each student determine the smallest sizes at which he can identify conspicuous minerals, describe shapes, and estimate diameters.

2. The quantitative distribution of grain size is measured by passing a weighed sample through a graduated series of sieves and weighing the fraction retained by each mesh. Even if the work does not call for these data, it is an advantage to prepare a set of screened samples to serve as standards. They are useful for comparison against both loose and consolidated clastic material and also for the tactile impressions each grade imparts when rolled between the fingers. It is desirable to label the standard samples with sizes stated in millimeters rather than mesh numbers.

3. To examine finer sediments and those containing argillaceous matter, one can follow the procedure suggested at the end of the previous chapter for the study of soil; the clay fraction is removed by repeated washing and decanting.

4. Some graywackes, especially those that are firmly consolidated, closely resemble fine-grained dolerite. This difficulty can be overcome by direct comparison of the rocks involved. Even if the lens fails to reveal the presence of clastic grains in the graywacke, the handling of the rocks will easily disclose their differences in specific gravity.

   The distinction between some arkoses and granitic igneous rocks that have been weakened and rendered friable by weathering may also be difficult, and it may be necessary to crush small samples for better observation of quartz and feldspar. Also, in most arkose the percentage of quartz runs higher than in the igneous rocks with which they might be confused.

5. In describing rocks with fossils, the following are matters for observation and description:
   a. Kind of organisms.
   b. Whether intact, broken, or abraded.
   c. Mode of preservation (molds, casts, silicified, etc.).
   d. Distribution with respect to bedding.
   e. Whether bound to matrix or easily separable.

6. The theoretical volume and weight changes that attend the conversion of limestone to dolomite are calculated in Appendix B. Similar computations are useful to illustrate other types of diagenesis. The dehydration of gypsum to form anhydrite provides a simple example.

7. Since porosity is a larger and more important factor in sedimentary rocks than in most others, it calls for a correspondingly larger share of consideration. Problems such as the following call attention to the dis-

tinction between *bulk density* and the density of the components and to the effect of porosity upon the former:

A specimen of porous sandstone weighs 322 g when completely dry. With all the openings filled with water its weight is 349 g. Its volume, including pore space, is 142 cc. Find:

a. The porosity (per cent of pore space, by volume).
b. The specific gravity of the dry rock, but including the pore spaces (this is the bulk density).
c. The specific gravity of the rock with all spaces filled by water.
d. The specific gravity of the solid rock, excluding pores.

·9·

Metamorphic Rocks

When a rock of any origin has been visibly changed by high temperatures, or by high pressures, or by fluids acting under these conditions, the resulting product is a metamorphic rock. The new properties that a rock acquires have come about to establish a condition of equilibrium within the changed environment. The manner of the reorganization and its degree depend upon the combination of factors that control the metamorphism and also upon their magnitude. However, the response of a rock to the changed circumstances is limited by the chemical and physical properties of the rock being affected and by whatever substances may be introduced as a part of the metamorphic process. More simply, the pattern of a metamorphic rock is set by these variable factors: (1) the nature of the original material, (2) the particular modifying process or processes, and (3) the intensity with which these influences have operated.

Of all rocks, the metamorphics are the most difficult to account for, because the petrologist has no opportunity to watch the metamorphic processes in action, and laboratory technique has not yet made it possible to deal simultaneously with the pressures and temperatures needed to simulate the conditions under which most metamorphic rocks are formed. By the time they come into man's zone of observation in an outcrop or underground working, a long interval of time has elapsed, erosion has removed an indefinite but considerable load of overlying rock, and they are situated where surface or near-surface temperatures and pressures prevail.

The first and most necessary step in the study of a metamorphic rock, or of any rock, is the examination and description of its components, and the manner in which they are assembled to give the rock its total pattern. The procedure with metamorphic rocks is only different in that their identification and interpretation calls for the closest attention to the shapes, the spacing, and the orientation of minerals. In the terminology of metamorphism it is becoming the custom to include all data that pertain to texture and structure in the single category of **fabric.*** It is to be emphasized that the fabric of a metamorphic rock is no less significant in its interpretation than is the mineralogy.

The goals of interpretation are to determine the constitution of the original rock, to identify the agents that promoted its change, and to attempt a restoration of the geologic conditions that prevailed during metamorphism. Not all metamorphic rocks lend themselves to a ready interpretation of their histories; similar rocks may result from rocks of different ancestry or represent different metamorphic processes. Other rocks may be so profoundly reorganized that no trace of the original habit remains, and the past of some is obscured by the action of more than one cycle of metamorphism.

CHARACTERISTICS OF METAMORPHIC ROCKS

The visible changes brought about by metamorphism are:

I The partial or complete reorganization of the constituents to form a new mineral assembly.

II A change in grain size, characteristically to produce a coarser texture.

III The development of new structures, particularly those manifested by various parallel arrangements of minerals.

---

* **Structural petrology** is a comparatively new branch of geology primarily concerned with the task of relating rock fabrics to the large-scale structures of which the rocks form a part. For instance, it endeavors to correlate the fabrics of deformed rock with the forces that caused the folding or metamorphism and to trace the movement of magma by observations on the flow structures of igneous rocks. Structural petrology takes for its domain all rocks that contain constituents oriented by movement. Its methods are almost entirely statistical, a characteristic that it shares with many other successful techniques developed within the natural sciences during recent years. (Other examples in geology are sedimentation, paleontology, and a beginning in igneous petrology.)

These changes may occur alone, but more commonly they take place in various combinations. Usually they are obvious enough in the hand specimen to distinguish the metamorphic rocks from those formed in other ways. The bulk chemical composition of a rock may be maintained throughout metamorphism, but it may receive additions from without, or some materials may be expelled, or metasomatism may bring about an exchange. However, a change in composition can be inferred from megascopic evidence only if a rock contains veins or other structures that obviously consist of introduced substances, or when there are minerals with components foreign to the parent rock.

The Minerals of Metamorphic Rocks

The minerals that are common in metamorphic rocks and others that may occasionally be recognized in hand specimens are listed in Table 20. Their chemical formulas and specific gravities may be found in Table 8. Inasmuch as many metamorphic processes take place at high temperatures and under strong pressure, many of the minerals appearing in the list are also characteristic of the igneous rocks. The feldspathoids (leucite, nepheline, sodalite) and analcite are the only essential igneous rock minerals that are absent. Similarly, the list fails to include some weathering products (limonite, the clay minerals), and certain other constituents of the sedimentary rocks (opal, chalcedony, glauconite). These do not occur in metamorphic rocks because they are stable only in environments controlled by relatively low temperatures and pressures.

The minerals that are particularly characteristic* of metamorphic rocks are kyanite, andalusite, staurolite, and wollastonite. All these are formed under the influence of high temperature, high pressure, or both. Several other minerals (tremolite, actinolite, garnet) are not of themselves diagonostic of metamorphism, but are nevertheless far more conspicuous in metamorphic rocks than in associations formed in other ways. The garnets constitute an unusual group;

---

* Several other minerals that are almost entirely restricted to metamorphic rocks have been omitted, either because they are comparatively rare, or because they can seldom be identified megascopically. Minerals excluded for these reasons are sillimanite, chloritoid, cordierite, vesuvianite, and scapolite.

TABLE 20. Minerals in Metamorphic Rocks

Mineral	Genesis	Occurrence
Quartz	May be introduced, a recrystallization product or a relict mineral	Widespread: in schists, gneisses, quartzite, etc.
Feldspars	Common as a result of thermal metamorphism, and as introduced material	In gneisses, schists, and rocks produced by contact metamorphism and injection metamorphism
Hornblende	Most often formed by the metamorphism of femic rocks	In schists, amphibolites and some gneisses
Tremolite Actinolite	Chiefly derived from the recrystallization of dolomitic rocks at moderate to high temperatures	In schists and marbles
Olivine	Formed by thermal metamorphism of dolomite	Marbles (ophicalcite)
Diopside	Similar in origin to olivine, but formed at higher temperatures	Chiefly in diopside marbles. The other monoclinic pyroxenes are largely confined to rocks so profoundly metamorphosed that they are frequently indistinguishable from igneous rocks
Wollastonite	Formed by the high-temperature metamorphism of limestone	In marbles formed by contact metamorphism
Muscovite	Usually the result of metamorphism at comparatively low temperature, derived from argillaceous sediments and rocks containing alkali feldspars	In slates, phyllites, schists
Biotite	Similar in origin to muscovite, but formed at higher temperatures	In schists and gneisses
Phlogopite	Formed from argillaceous, dolomitic sediments, and possibly from femic rocks	Less common than muscovite and biotite in schists, but conspicuous in some impure marbles
Hematite	Formed from iron rich sediments and as an introduced mineral	Occurs as specularite in iron-rich schists, and as an introduced mineral in contact metamorphic deposits
Magnetite	Similar to hematite from which it may be derived, but representing more intense conditions of metamorphism	As streaks, lenses, and irregular masses in metamorphosed iron formations, also either disseminated or as segregations in contact metamorphic deposits
Calcite	Inherited from original rock, but almost invariably recrystallized; also formed from dolomite when the magnesia of this compound enters other minerals	In marbles and ophicalcites
Dolomite	Usually inherited from original rock	In dolomitic marbles
Graphite	Derived from the carbonaceous substances contained in sedimentary rocks	In slates, phyllites, schists, and some impure marbles

194

TABLE 20.   Minerals in Metamorphic Rocks (*Continued*)

Mineral	Genesis	Occurrence
Chlorite	Formed either by hydrothermal alteration, or low-temperature metamorphism from biotite and similar complex alumino-silicates	In slates, phyllites, and schists
"Serpentine"	Chiefly a product of hydrothermal alteration, in metamorphic rocks; usually a later product derived from olivine or nonaluminous pyroxene	In hydrothermally altered femic igneous rocks and in serpentine marbles
Talc	Formed by low-temperature metamorphism and by hydrothermal alteration; principally derived from femic rock material	In schists and soapstones
Epidote	Formed at moderate temperatures where the necessary lime, alumina, and silica occur in suitable proportions	Common in schists and in limestones that have been metamorphosed, but seldom a conspicuous mineral
Almandite	Formed under the influence of strong pressure and moderate to high temperature	Principally in mica and hornblende schists
Grossularite	Develops at high temperature where the necessary components are available	In rocks produced by thermal metamorphism of calcareous sediments
Andradite	Formed by high-temperature metamorphism	In limestones affected by contact metamorphism
Andalusite	Formed by high-temperature thermal metamorphism of argillaceous material	In hornfels
Kyanite	A product of high temperature and high (directed) pressure	In schists
Staurolite	A product of high temperature and high (directed) pressure	In schists
Pyrite	Pyrite is the stable form of iron sulfide in any metamorphic environment except those where the highest temperatures prevail	Pyrite is ubiquitous, but is particularly common in slates, phyllites, and rocks produced by contact metamorphism

their compositions vary widely, but it is impossible to tell them apart megascopically and even difficult to identify them with refined laboratory methods. Nevertheless the compositions of the garnets of the metamorphic rocks should be noted since they are useful to illustrate chemical reactions that proceed in metamorphic processes. Almandite ($Fe_3Al_2Si_4O_{12}$) is the common garnet of schists, but also occurs in pegmatite. Grossularite ($Ca_3Al_2Si_4O_{12}$) and andradite ($Ca_3Fe_2Si_4O_{12}$) are both formed at high temperatures, the former as the result of the metamorphism of argillaceous limestones, the latter by the introduction of igneous emanations as part of the metamorphism of limestone.

Chlorite, serpentine, and talc are all hydrated magnesium silicates. They may be formed from the femic minerals of igneous rocks or from similar minerals in metamorphic rocks that have been derived from impure dolomites. Chlorite differs from the others in containing aluminum and so is usually related to biotite or aluminous amphiboles. These minerals develop at comparatively low temperatures and in the absence of strong pressure. All of them contain a large amount of water. In some associations they appear as products of relatively mild metamorphism, in others as the results of hydrothermal alteration; however, it is not always possible to differentiate between the two processes. The genesis of epidote is similar. It may be formed through the hydrothermal alteration of lime-bearing feldspar or crystallize as a distinctly metamorphic mineral.

Texture of Metamorphic Rocks

As metamorphism progresses, there is a general tendency toward an increase in grain size. Recrystallization encourages the growth of large crystals at the expense of the smaller. This takes place both when the minerals of the original association are being transformed to new compounds and when the mineral composition remains unchanged. Consequently most metamorphic rocks consist of visible crystals. An excessively fine-textured metamorphic rock can usually be attributed to relatively mild metamorphism but is not necessarily formed from an originally fine-grained rock. (Purely mechanical metamorphism may grind a coarse rock to powder.)

The textures of most metamorphic rocks differ from those of igneous rocks and the clastic sediments, chiefly in the way the minerals fit together. This can be seen best by comparing specimens of the three classes of rocks with minerals large enough to be plainly visible (Figure 23). The minerals of igneous rocks crystallize in a more or less orderly sequence, and consequently they are prevailingly interlocked, with the last minerals fitting into whatever spaces have remained for them. They make a jigsaw pattern, with some pieces straight, some irregular, and some both. The grains of clastic sediments seldom meet in intimate contact, rather they touch tangentially, and the remaining space is filled by some bonding material. In contrast to these, the metamorphic minerals for the most part fit together without a paste and without interlocking. (Some marbles and some quartzites are exceptions.) Some metamorphic rocks show arrangements comparable to stone walls, built without mortar; others resemble walls made of ill-laid, odd-sized, brick that have subsequently sagged and slumped. A few look like mosaics, with the tiles fitted together neatly, but without a plan.

Textures that result directly from metamorphism are described as **crystalloblastic.** A few metamorphic minerals have a strong tend-

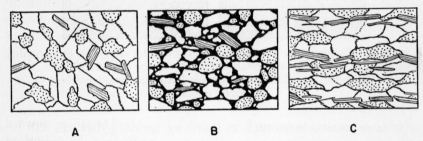

A   B   C

FIGURE 23. **A,** contrasted textures of granite. **B,** sandstone. **C,** gneiss. The crystals of the granite are interlocked, the sandstone grains touch tangentially, and the minerals of the gneiss form a mosaic with a limited amount of interlocking. Symbols: quartz (dotted), feldspar (blank), mica (lined), cement in sandstone (black).

ency to develop well-formed crystals; this is marked in garnet and staurolite, less conspicuous in the amphiboles and kyanite. Minerals bounded by crystal faces are **idioblastic;** those lacking crystal form are **xenoblastic.** These terms are analogous to the adjectives *euhedral* and *anhedral* used in igneous rock descriptions, but they do not connote similar origins. **Porphyroblasts** are minerals in metamorphic rocks conspicuously larger than the surrounding material, but unlike the phenocrysts of igneous rocks they are usually formed at a late rather than at an early stage in the development of the rock. Porphyroblasts often contain mineral inclusions large enough to be seen easily and sometimes clearly arranged in lines or planes. When the enclosing rock is characterized by a parallel structure, the porphyroblasts may interrupt the grain, cutting it sharply and cleanly (Figure

197

24), or the adjacent minerals may curve around the porphyroblasts as though they had been forced aside.

If metamorphism fails to bring about the complete reorganization of a rock, some of its original characteristics may escape destruction. A **relict** mineral is one that can be identified as a survivor of an earlier regime, but it is not the custom to apply this term to unreduced

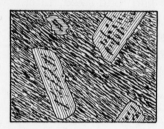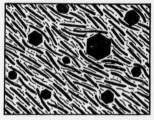

FIGURE 24.   Porphyroblasts. **Left,** crystals, developing later than the foliation, have cut the schistosity and retain remnants of the earlier minerals as inclusions. **Right,** the crystallization of garnets has forced aside and bent the enclosing micas.

pebbles or to structures such as fossils or bedding that can still be seen.

Because many of the structures in metamorphic rocks are directly dependent upon the shapes of the minerals, these should be observed closely in the examination of a rock and included, with their dimensions, in the description. Common shapes that are distinct enough to be seen clearly are:

1. Flakes, or thin plates: the micas, chlorite, talc, graphite, specularite.
2. Prisms, some stout and columnar, others flat and bladed: staurolite, tremolite, actinolite, hornblende, kyanite.
3. Equidimensional: garnet, calcite, dolomite, frequently feldspar and quartz.

The Structures of Metamorphic Rocks

The description of the metamorphic rocks is simplified by dividing them into two groups, one including all rocks with parallel structures and a second group with no visible evidence of parallel arrangement. This is an arbitrary segregation, made purely for convenience. For some rocks it has a genetic significance, but it should not be used as a basis for classification, because many rocks that appear isotropic to the unaided eye actually consist of minerals with parallel arrangements that can be discovered only by special techniques.

All the ordinary parallel structures found in rocks can be related to planes or to lines or to some combination of these. In field work, the attitude of a set of parallel planes is measured and recorded as dip and strike; it is the same method that is applied to bedding, faults, and joints. The observations are plotted on maps with the strike and dip symbol, modified, if necessary, to show that they refer to metamorphic structures. A linear structure is described in much the same way, but since it has no equivalent to strike, it is indicated by a single arrow, pointed to indicate its (downward) direction and accompanied by a number to record the angle of inclination. The actual field measurements are sometimes difficult to make; the necessary technique is described in standard books dealing with structural geology and field geology.

The most common structures are described below as arrangements or patterns, and without reference to their origin. Some of these are shown diagrammatically in Figure 25.

I. Minerals of flaky habit may be oriented with their flat surfaces mutually parallel. Because of their shapes, biotite, muscovite, chlorite, and talc lend themselves readily to this pattern. Since each of these minerals cleaves in the flat direction, a rock in which they are aligned breaks easily in the parallel plane. This parallel orientation with its closely linked direction of fracture is the common structure of many slates, all phyllites and nearly all schists. **Foliation** is the general term to describe the resulting structure, but in schists it may be called **schistosity**, and in slates, **slaty foliation** provided the mineral parallelism can be seen. *Cleavage* should be restricted to its mineralogical meaning and to those rocks that break cleanly along smooth parallel planes. (In some slates the cleavage is not related to foliation.)

II. Foliation that results from flat parallel minerals may be further modified if the longest of the three dimensions of the

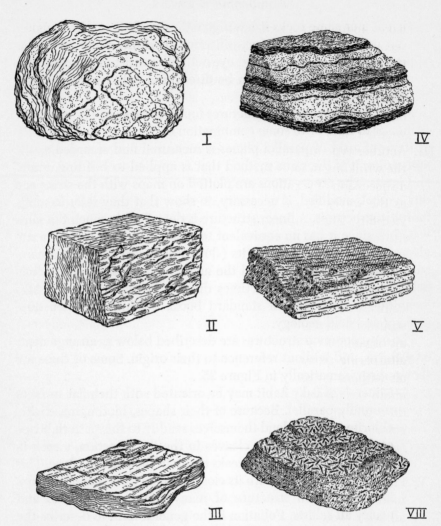

FIGURE 25. Parallel structures in metamorphic rocks. Numbers refer to the corresponding paragraphs on pages 199–202. **I**, parallel arrangement of minerals with flaky habit; **II**, the same, with longest dimensions of flakes aligned; **III**, lineation resulting from corrugation in schistose or slaty foliation; **IV**, alternate bands of schistose and granular habit; **V**, prismatic minerals in parallel alignment, but not segregated in bands; **VIII**, prismatic minerals with long axes in parallel planes, but otherwise arranged at random. Drawn by Paul Dobbs.

200

flakes lie in approximately parallel positions. This introduces a second metamorphic structure, a linear parallelism that lies in the plane of foliation. This, as well as any other alignment of linear elements, is called **lineation.** The one just described is difficult to see on fresh surfaces, but is more frequently visible on outcrops that have been etched or selectively stained by weathering.

III. Another type of lineation combined with foliation, appears as the wrinkling or undulation of the foliation planes. It is seen as a succession of parallel folds, with amplitudes almost as coarse as the waves in corrugated iron, down to the lowest limit of visibility. These crenulations are particularly common in phyllite and not uncommon in schist and slate. In fine-grained rocks they can best be observed by turning a foliation surface so that it reflects the light from a succession of varying angles.

IV. Many gneisses and some schists consist of alternate bands of contrasting minerals, thus giving the rock a laminate (but not stratified) structure. Usually one set of bands contains minerals organized by one or more types of parallelism, whereas the alternating members are made up of equidimensional minerals without visible orientation. Although fine texture may preclude the identification of the parallel arrangement, it is seldom absent from bands that are either micaceous or dark colored. The laminate structure may be complexly and tightly folded, so that several folds are visible in a single hand specimen.

V. Prismatic minerals, especially amphibole, may be disposed more or less evenly through a rock, independent of planes, but all with their long axes parallel. This structure is a form of lineation, and rocks possessing it break fairly evenly in any direction that includes the prisms. Its most usual occurrence is in gneisses, where the amphibole is associated with mixtures of apparently unoriented feldspar and quartz.

VI. A lineation, similar to the one above, consist of narrow streaks of minerals, or mineral fragments, strung through a rock as discontinuous but parallel lines.

VII. Prismatic minerals may be distributed with their long axes parallel, but at the same time concentrated in recognizable planes. The structure is similar to that described above, as II, but is controlled by prismatic instead of flat minerals.

VIII. Prismatic minerals may lie in planes, but without parallel orientation of the long axes, like matches scattered at random on a flat surface.

The remaining structures show no visible dependence on mineral shape or arrangement, but this does not imply that mineral orientation is either absent or has exerted no control.

IX. Some rocks break, either easily or with difficulty, along definite parallel planes. There may be more than one direction of such fracture, and it occurs in rocks that may or may not in clude foliation or another type of observable parallelism. When the structure can be seen on a surface inclined to the plane of fracture, it may give the appearance of a series of closely spaced faults or joints, and it may resemble bedding. Formerly it was described as *fracture cleavage,* but this term is gradually being abondoned by those investigators who find that it is either too restrictive or includes too much. In fine-grained rocks it cannot always be distinguished from a true slaty foliation controlled by minute flakes of mica or chlorite.

X. Lineation may result from the alignment of the long axes of fusiform, ellipsoidal or less regular, but nevertheless inequidimensional bodies in a rock. This elongation may occur with foliation or in its absence. In some metamorphic rocks, these objects are clearly pebbles that have been deformed ("stretched" or "rolled out"); in others they are mineral aggregates or single minerals that have been drawn out during metamorphism. (Similarly, elongated oolites have provided much data in the petrofabric analysis of folded sedimentary rocks.)

A rock that shows no sign of parallel structure, either in its minerals or the way it breaks, can be described as *massive.* However much of the evidence of parallelism is elusive, it should be sought with care on all the sides of a specimen and, wherever possible, on both fresh and weathered surfaces.

202

METAMORPHIC ROCKS

Rock Names

In the everyday vocabulary of geology there are very few rock names available to designate metamorphic products with specific characteristics; most of the terms call attention to a single outstanding attribute. Thus slate and schist are rocks distinguished from others by their structural habits; marble and quartzite refer to the compositions of carbonate and quartzose rocks. On the other hand, **mylonite** signifies a rock that has been crushed and pulverized by movement under the influence of strong pressure, and hence the term implies metamorphic history rather than composition or structure. Consequently the name applied to a given rock conveys little information unless it includes qualifying terms to restrict its meaning. Examples of compounded names are: *graywacke slate,* designating the original material; *biotite schist,* in which biotite is the conspicuous mineral; *granitic gneiss,* suggesting a mineral association; *migmatite gneiss,* referring to a process (the intimate mixing of invading magmatic fluids with country rock). The prefix *meta-* is sometimes used to designate the original rock, as in *metagabbro* for a metamorphic rock that was formerly gabbro. Similarly *orthoschists* and *orthogneisses* are schists and gneisses formed from igneous rocks, and *paraschists* and *paragneisses* are those derived from sedimentary material.

If our knowledge of metamorphism were sufficiently complete, names might be devised to yield all of the following information:

1. The original material.
2. The kind of metamorphism imposed upon it.
3. The degree of metamorphism.
4. As a result of these three factors, the mineral association, texture, and structure.

The rock would then be classified genetically and described as well. An understanding of the natural history of metamorphism such as this ideal implies, is a goal for the future, and until it is more closely approached the naming of a metamorphic rock must continue to depend primarily on characteristics that can be directly observed. The extent to which the history of a metamorphic rock can be inferred from its mineralogy, texture, and structure can be judged only after a consideration of the metamorphic processes.

Table 21 lists the chief types of metamorphic rock. Most of them can usually be identified by megascopic methods, but some (granulite, some gneisses, amphibolite, eclogite) may be indistinguishable from igneous rocks of similar appearance and can only be classified

TABLE 21.   Metamorphic Rocks

Rocks with Visible Parallel Structure* (Foliates and banded rocks)	
Slate	Schist (continued)
Mylonite (in part)	tremolite-
Phyllite	actinolite-
Schist	staurolite-
muscovite-	graphitic
chlorite-	Gneiss
talc-	granitic, diorite, etc.
biotite-	hornblende-
quartz-mica-	biotite-
garnetiferous-	banded
hornblende	augen-

Rocks without Parallel Structure*	
Quartzite	Soapstone
Marble	Amphibolite
dolomitic	Granulite
serpentine-, etc.	Eclogite
Hornfels	

┌ * In the sense used here, structure refers only to arrangements that result from metamorphism and does not include primary structures such as bedding, which sometimes can be traced in metamorphic rocks.

as metamorphic if their field relationships are known. This uncertainty is not always confined to the laboratory or to rocks studied megascopically, for there are many actual places and also inferred circumstances where it is not yet possible to draw a line of separation between the results of igneous and metamorphic processes. The segregation of metamorphic rocks in Table 21, into one group with visible parallel structures, and another without, has no genetic significance. The distinction is made only to facilitate description.

Slate

Slate is a predominantly aphanitic metamorphic rock that breaks readily in at least one direction, but it does not necessarily separate into smooth plane sheets. The easy parting may result from the parallel orientation of micaceous minerals or chlorite or from closely spaced, parallel, incipient fractures (fracture cleavage). A true foliation plane, caused by parallel minerals, can usually be recognized by the characteristic gloss that mica and chlorite contribute to its surfaces. If there are two directions of weakness, foliation and fracture cleavage, or two sets of incipient fractures, their intersection divides the rock into prisms or tapering wedgelike forms.

In many slates derived from sedimentary rock the stratification may still be followed. Differences in the original beds may show as bands of contrasting color or as layers of different texture. Faint lines may trace the bedding planes of more homogeneous strata. Similarly, but less frequently, other original structures can be seen, such as distorted fossils or suggestions of a previous igneous or metamorphic habit.

Lineation is common. It may occur as a subdued wrinkling visible on the foliation planes or as the intersection between any plane structures; foliation, fracture, or bedding.

The slate most widely used for roofing has made "slate blue" a generally understood color term. Other colors are green (from chlorite), and various shades of red and tan when finely divided iron oxides are present. Biotite, andalusite, and graphite may occur as porphyroblasts, but they usually take the form of small lumps or knots and cannot be identified megascopically. Pyrite, however, is common, although it is probably an introduced mineral rather than a porphyroblast. It is found as isolated crystals, as small disseminated grains, or in thin veins.

To be suitable for roofing, a slate must break easily in one direction only. This parting should be a true foliation and should permit the separation of the rock into reasonably smooth, plane sheets of the required thickness. Also it must be free from porphyroblasts, and from pyrite and any other minerals that weather easily. These specifications are included to indicate that the rock used for roofing is a narrowly restricted substance; it is not the norm for slate.

Most slates are formed by the metamorphism of argillaceous sediments, but they can be derived from volcanic ash and other fine grained rocks. Coarse-textured rocks can be turned to slate only if there has been sufficient movement to pulverize the rock.

Schist and Phyllite

Schists occur in great variety. They are most conveniently separated by prefixing the name of the mineral that is most conspicuous, abundant, or significant in interpreting the metamorphic history. This system has the merits of being easily understood and remembered, and since it permits the use of more than one mineral qualifier, it is also flexible. Examples of compounded names are *staurolite-mica-schist* and *garnetiferous biotite-schist*.

The texture of schist is crystalloblastic, but quartz and other stable minerals may escape transformation and appear as relics. Grain size varies, but even in a relatively fine-textured schist most of the minerals can be seen, even though a lens is required to make them visible and some may not be identified. On the other hand, a coarsely crystalline rock usually contains some minerals that are too small for megascopic observation. Garnet, usually almandite, is by far the most common porphyroblast, and occasionally constitutes most of the rock. Staurolite is found in some schists, but porphyroblasts of other minerals are rare. Some schists (hornblende-, chlorite-, talc-) approach a monomineralic composition but most schists consist of at least two minerals.

Foliation, contributed by the parallel orientation of flat or prismatic minerals, is the outstanding characteristic of schist. The principal minerals are the micas, the amphiboles, chlorite, and talc. Their distribution and arrangement control the specific qualities of the foliation. Thus a rock will break readily and more or less smoothly if the minerals are closely spaced and if their parallelism has attained a high degree of order. Conversely, the foliation may be barely recognizable if the minerals with the necessary shapes are either few or less uniformly aligned. In considering an entire outcrop, the foliation may be uniform enough to be treated as a plane,

but in the individual specimen the foliation of schist is usually irregular. It may be rough because of imperfectly aligned minerals,
wavy on a coarse scale, or finely wrinkled. If these undulations present a parallel pattern, they constitute an element of lineation. Another type of lineation results from the parallel arrangement of the
long axes of amphiboles and similarly shaped minerals. This lineation may lie in the foliation plane, or may exist as an independent
direction in the absence of an actual foliation structure. This last
condition is illustrated by the rocks that consist of oriented hornblende crystals and little else. These rocks are classified as schists
even when they include no planar foliation.

Because schists, in general, are products of more intense metamorphism than the slates, they retain fewer structures inherited
from their premetamorphic state. Evidence of bedding, for instance,
is seldom visible in the hand specimen, although it can sometimes
be traced in the field as bands of contrasting lithology. For the same
reason it is more difficult to identify the rock from which a schist has
been derived.

In many regions the schists have been intimately invaded by fluids
of magmatic origin, and hence are mixed rocks, with some of their
characteristics determined by the metamorphic minerals and fabric,
and others resulting from the crystallization of igneous minerals.
These rocks and gneisses with a similar history are collectively
known as **migmatites,** a term that signifies mixing. Often the invaded
rock has been so completely soaked by the entering fluid, that the
resulting material is too homogeneous to show its twofold origin,
and hence it is not always possible to recognize a migmatite. There
are two useful and reasonably common criteria for such igneous injection: (a) large euhedral feldspar crystals that have grown across
the foliation and contain bits of schist minerals as inclusions, and
(b) lenses, pods, or stringers consisting of quartz and feldspar, arranged concordantly within the foliation (Figure 26).

Phyllite is a transitional rock between slate and schist, with a texture (grain size) intermediate between them, and more or less wavy
foliation controlled by chlorite or micaceous minerals. It lacks the
homogeneous appearance of slate, but unlike schist, the individual
minerals are not megascopically visible. Lineation due either to

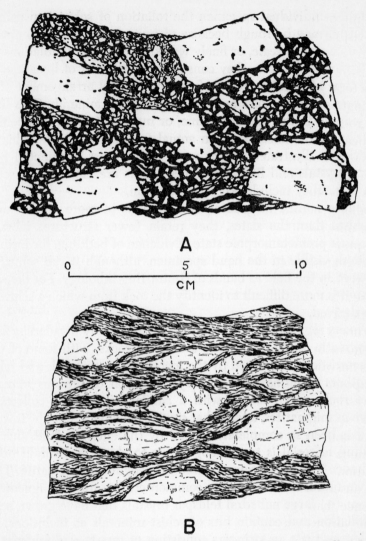

0   5   10

CM

FIGURE 26. Migmatites. **A**, large and well-formed feldspars crystallized from igneous fluids that have invaded biotite schist. The surrounding material is an intimate mixture of schist and introduced material. The foliation has been obscured. The feldspars enclose scattered biotite flakes. **B**, lit-par-lit invasion of schist. The podlike lenses of introduced material are alkali feldspar.

wrinkling or to the intersection of fractures or bedding is nearly always visible on the foliation surfaces.

Gneiss

The term gneiss is loosely used to embrace many different mineral combinations and a variety of structures, and it includes a great many rocks of uncertain origin. Gneisses are named in various ways: to indicate parentage (*conglomerate gneiss*), composition (*granitic gneiss*), to emphasize a distinctive mineral (*kyanite gneiss*), or a conspicuous structure (*augen gneiss*). In its narrowest meaning, gneiss is defined as a feldspathic, phaneric, metamorphic rock, with a parallel structure that assumes the form of streaks or bands.

The minerals, the texture, and the structure are purely matters for description and can be determined with an accuracy and completeness that are limited only by the methods and skill of the observer. The origin is a complex question, made particularly so because the gneisses that are both most common and most abundant are rocks of granitic or near-granitic composition. In many of them the parallel structure is manifested by the alignment of femic minerals, an arrangement by no means restricted to rocks of metamorphic origin. Rocks answering this description, presumably with various histories, are exposed over wide areas, particularly in the older terranes.

Investigators who have dealt with the granitic gneisses have submitted several explanations for their origin. For some specific rocks, one or another of these explanations is generally accepted, within the limits of doubt that are implicit in the acceptance of any "explanation" in natural science, but the genesis of many of these rocks is an unsettled question calling for further investigation and clearer evidence than yet has been forthcoming.

The various geologic interpretations advanced to account for the gneisses and the rocks that resemble them are summarized in the following paragraphs. Although the summaries emphasize the genesis of granitic rocks, some of them apply equally to rocks that are not preponderantly quartz-feldspar mixtures. From the explanations it will be clear that some of the rocks in question are igneous, others plainly metamorphic, and that many are rocks of mixed origins. Occasionally a specimen will exhibit evidence to justify its assignment to a specific origin, but far more often the history can be interpreted only through its field relationships. Gneisses and the rocks that simulate gneiss are difficult; too frequently they can be understood only in a most general way.

I. *Igneous (Granitic) Intrusions with Primary Flow Structure*

Movement within a crystallizing magma may line up biotite or hornblende in the direction of flow, just before final consolidation locks the minerals into set positions. In the field, the flow structure is most clearly seen near the contacts. Here it is usually found parallel to the walls of the intrusion, following whatever iregularities may be present. Farther away, toward the interior of the intrusion, the parallelism may be obscure or fail to show at all by megascopic methods. The igneous origin of rocks with primary flow is implied by describing them as *gneissoid* or *gneissic* granite (or quartz-diorite, etc.), since "gneiss" used as a name rather than a qualifying term indicates a metamorphic rock.

II. *Metamorphosed Granite*

In other rocks, presumed also to be igneous intrusions, the parallel arrangement of dark minerals has been attributed to metamorphism. Under this hypothesis, the original granite was squeezed sufficiently to rotate and orient the flat and prismatic minerals, and the subsequent reorganization of the entire rock then erased all signs of crushing or other corroborating evidence of metamorphism. This explanation seems open to question, except possibly when applied to small bodies of rock, for large granite masses are generally regarded as resistant elements in the earth's crust; geologic evidence indicates that they yield only by faulting. If such rocks exist, they may properly be described as *granite gneiss.*

III. *Migmatites*

Many gneisses are migmatites (p. 207); rocks invaded by mobile igneous emanations. The typical migmatite gneiss is a rock formed by the intrusion of igneous substance into foliate metamorphic rocks, especially the schists, less often into phyllites and slates. The igneous fluids, in following the schistosity, separate the foliae and so divide the rock into alternate and more or less parallel bands of igneous and metamorphic minerals. The process is called *lit-par-lit* intrusion; its effects are indicated diagrammatically in Figure 19. In many such rocks the contacts between invaded and invading substances are clean

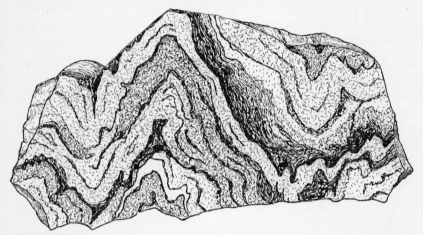

FIGURE 27. Injection gneiss with complex folds. The darker streaks represent the invaded schist, the lighter bands consist of introduced quartz and feldspar.

and conformable. The igneous fluids normally crystallize as quartz-feldspar mixtures. In biotite or hornblende schists that have been thus invaded, the contrast between light and dark minerals produces a strong banded appearance; one that is particularly striking when the rock is closely folded (Figure 27).

The process, as outlined this far, includes only the mechanical step of intrusion. Usually, however, it is accompanied by chemical effects in which the minerals of the invaded rock are transformed to new compounds by reaction with the igneous fluids. In the simplest case, the minerals are changed by replacement with no reorganization of structure other than the change from a schistose rock to one that is banded. Proceeding farther, the original minerals may be largely assimilated within the invading magma, and the banding may be obscured so that the lit-par-lit relationship is no longer clear. At a still later stage of the process, only a faint streaking may remain as an inheritance from the structure of the original rock. Granitization is complete, and specimens of the rock would be indistinguishable from gneissoid granite. The ultimate stage would be represented by a massive granite showing no outward evidence of a history of assimilation.

IV. *Nonigneous Granitization*

According to several groups of petrologists, most granite masses have been formed by replacement. The several hypotheses call for processes different from that outlined in the last paragraph essentially in the nature of the substances that bring about granitization. Instead of appealing to fluid emanations from a near-by granitic intrusion, they postulate the rise of even more highly mobile substances from sources deep within the crust of the earth. These have been considered by some to be extremely tenuous fluids. Others attribute granitization to ions, migrating upward by diffusion, and not transported by liquid or gaseous media.

Granitization, by whatever methods it may be achieved, has come to be a generally recognized process. The evidence for it rests in the many examples of transition between granite and foliate metamorphic rock, and the transition is attested by rocks in all the intermediate stages of chemical and mechanical mixing.

V. *Gneiss* (sensu stricto)

Gneisses with histories uncomplicated by the entrance of igneous matter or other invasions and not produced as some modification of granite may nevertheless resemble the rocks just described. Since the continents are essentially granitic (sialic), it is safe to assume that their waste, the products of decay and erosion, have the same composition. When these substances, the sedimentary rocks, are reorganized by intense metamorphism, it seems entirely reasonable that they should recrystallize as quartz-feldspar-mica-or-hornblende aggregates, for the stability of this mineral association under conditions of high temperature and pressure is demonstrated by the existence of granite itself. Nonsedimentary rocks such as salic tuffs and flows may be metamorphosed under similar conditions to produce similar gneisses.

Gneisses formed from sedimentary rocks or from layered tuffs and lava flows differ from schists in two characteristics; they contain a larger amount of feldspar and exhibit banded structures or linear streaking instead of close folia-tion. Also gneisses are believed to form in response to higher temperatures and higher pres-sures than attend the making of the schists and slates, and for this reason inherited structures are rare. In this connection, two types of gneiss are of interest, *conglomerate gneiss* and *augen gneiss.* Conglomerate gneiss contains pebbles that survive as ovoid or lenticular patches of quartz (Figure 28). Augen gneiss is similar, but includes conspicuous minerals or min-

FIGURE 28. Metaconglomerate, slightly reduced. Although the quartz pebbles have been deformed, broken, and some-what crushed, many have retained their rounded outlines. The matrix has been reorganized as a dark granular mosaic, without megascopically identifiable min-erals, but with an obscure parallelism.

eral aggregates scattered through the rock. These are relics of re-sistant minerals, phenocrysts or patches of the original rock that have not been completely obscured by the metamorphism. The au-gen, like the pebbles, take the form of thick or thin lenses, and also like the pebbles they may be fractured, granulated, or recrystallized. The long axes of both pebbles and augen are aligned with the paral-lel trend of the rock, but otherwise they do not participate in the foliation. Rather they resemble knots in wood about which the grain appears to curve and swirl.

Granulite, Amphibolite, Eclogite

Rocks without visible parallel orientation, but otherwise similar to gneiss in texture, mineralogy, and presumably in history, are called **granulite.** Megascopically, and even with the microscope, many granulites cannot be told apart from granite. As a rule they tend to be more equigranular than granite, and pyroxene may take the place of biotite or hornblende, but these criteria are suggestive only, and are by no means final. The origin of granulite is obscure; it is a part of the problem involving the history of granitic gneisses.

Amphibolite is a massive metamorphic rock made up principally of unoriented hornblende crystals. Except for the absence of foliation or lineation it is similar to hornblende schist. **Eclogite** is a less common rock consisting of garnet and a pyroxene. Chemical analyses show that its composition is close to basalt and consequently it has been regarded as metamorphosed basalt. However, the geologic association of some eclogites have led to their interpretation as igneous rocks. The specific gravities of garnet and pyroxene make eclogite one of the heaviest silicate rocks.

Quartzite and Marble

The name quartzite, standing alone, signifies a metamorphic rock composed chiefly of quartz that has undergone recrystallization. Its strength and durability come partly from the properties of quartz and partly from the intimate interlocking of its crystals. Pure quartzite is white, others are colored by various oxides and silicates of iron. If pebbles are recognizable, the rock is a *conglomerate quartzite.* (*Quartzite conglomerate* would indicate a sedimentary rock with quartzite pebbles.)

Quartz schist is a predominantly quartzose rock with enough muscovite in parallel alignment to provide the necessary foliate structure. In this rock the quartz may be completely recrystallized, as in most quartzite, or it may be granulated, as though by strong movement.

The marbles, including the dolomitic marbles, are all visibly crystalline, with textures ranging from finely saccaharoidal to extremely coarse. The colors depend upon the amount and kind of materials associated with the original limestone—carbonaceous substances yield gray or black rocks, iron compounds give shades of green or red. In the absence of coloring agents, both calcite and dolomitic marbles are white. Many minerals are found in marbles derived from limestones with mixed compositions. Some of these are: diopside, serpentine (often altered from olivine), phlogopite, and graphite. Highly serpentinous marble is known as **ophicalcite.**

Hornfels

Hornfels is an argillaceous rock, clay, shale, or slate that has been baked. Usually a hornfels has undergone enough recrystallization to be compact and hard, but it remains aphanitic. Bedding and other structures may be well preserved and easily visible. Sandy layers intercalated with the argillaceous beds appear faintly granular and lighter colored against the background of denser and darker hornfels. Either biotite or andalusite porphyroblasts may occur, or the rock may be spotted with small knots of graphite.

Serpentine and Soapstone

Serpentine is a massive soft, greenish or gray rock with a few other distinctive attributes. The texture may be fine or fibrous, and in some specimens it is possible to make out traces of an earlier crystalline or granular habit. Slickensided surfaces are common in some serpentines. They appear to be oriented at random, and although they indicate movement they do not appear to be related to recognizable faults or fault systems.

Although the term "serpentine" is more correctly used to describe a rock, it is used also (and more frequently) to refer to the mineral serpentine ($H_4Mg_3Si_2O_9$). In fibrous form this mineral is *chrysotile*, the serpentine asbestos that occurs as veins in serpentine rock.

Soapstone is similar to serpentine in its fine texture and lack of visible structures, but it is softer and more nearly gray than green. The essential mineral is talc ($H_2Mg_3Si_3O_{12}$), to which the rock owes its softness and smoothness to the touch. Both serpentine and soapstone consist largely of hydrated magnesium silicates. In their common form they represent magnesian rocks that have been subjected to hydrothermal alteration.

METAMORPHIC PROCESSES AND EFFECTS

Whether one seeks to explain the origin of a single rock or attempts to survey the metamorphic rocks as a group, it is necessary to examine metamorphism in three distinct but related aspects of their genesis. In the first place, metamorphic rocks can be expected within several particular geologic settings, such as in "belts of strong folding" or "within the contact zone of an igneous intrusion." These and similar situations are understood in a broad and qualitative fashion. From them and from the rocks, certain conditions of stress have been inferred. These conditions also have not been described specifically, but their results are sufficiently uniform throughout the earth to have led to the establishment and broad definition of the various types of metamorphism (cataclastic, dynamothermal, etc.). Finally there is the actual reorganization of rock material. In these changes the geologic setting is relevant in that it determines the magnitude of the temperature and pressure factors, but the transformations themselves are analyzed as chemical and physical changes. This is the essence of metamorphism, and since high temperature and high pressures play the leading roles, it is appropriate to consider them first, reversing the historical order through which the knowledge of metamorphic rocks has evolved.

Metamorphic Agents: Temperature, Pressure, Fluids

The temperature within a rock may rise from several causes. The progressive temperature increase below the surface of the earth guarantees that a rock undergoing deeper burial will be warmed in accordance with the local geothermal gradient. Conduction and radiation from igneous bodies are other sources of heat and may be supplemented by the effects of hot fluids emanating from igneous intrusions. Heat is also generated by the friction that attends movement. The movements that play a part in metamorphic processes are related to pressure and can take place in several ways: between rock units or within them, between minerals, and within the crystal structure of minerals. Modern petrologists, however, tend to minimize this particular heat source in metamorphism on the grounds that most such movements occur so slowly that the heat would have ample time to escape, in spite of the low heat conductivity of rock. It is to be emphasized also that pressure, however great, does not generate heat of itself, but only indirectly as a result of ensuing movement.

Metamorphic Rocks

Any rock below the surface of the earth is subjected to a pressure that is at least the equivalent of the weight of the overlying rock. At shallow depths this can be regarded as pressure directed vertically downward. At deeper levels, presumably a few miles below the surface, the pressure due to burial is equalized, so that a rock is confined by pressures that are balanced on all sides. The condition is analogous to the "pressure at a point" within a liquid and is conveniently though not accurately described as *hydrostatic pressure.*

More important in metamorphism are the pressures directed more or less horizontally within the lithosphere. Whatever their origin, these are the forces involved in folding and thrusts, and in all other tectonic effects manifested by lateral squeezing and movement. From the evidence submitted by metamorphic rocks it seems clear that although the tangential pressure may not diminish, it tends to equalize in depth, as does the pressure resulting from burial.

Fluids may contribute actively to metamorphic processes, or they may serve merely to facilitate chemical change. Of the many substances that can exist in a fluid state in a metamorphic environment, water is by far the most abundant and significant, but carbon dioxide may participate as a mobile gas within certain limited conditions. Fluids entering a rock from igneous sources act as agents for the transfer of heat, and migrating fluids in general may introduce new substances, either through replacement or by direct addition. Few rocks, if any, are altogether free of water. Water may permeate the rocks as liquid or be combined with minerals such as the clays and micas. It is chiefly important as a medium for chemical exchange; reactions that proceed slowly in the dry state are greatly accelerated in the presence of water, even when this substance is not a part of either the initial or the final compounds. The general explanation for this phenomenon is that when the participating substances are in solution the ions are brought more quickly into the intimate contact that is necessary for their recombination. In metamorphism the process is aided also by high temperatures and the effect of pressure in increasing the solubility of minerals. As long as the water is not withdrawn by entering into solid compounds, it does not get "used up," so that a small quantity of water repeatedly used is sufficient to act

217

as the transfer medium in the recrystallization of a large amount of rock.

Reorganization of Rock Material

The reconstitution of rocks in metamorphic environments leads to new mineral associations, changed textures, and the development of characteristic structures. Although all three of the agents just described contribute to the total change, they are not all necessary factors in every type of metamorphism, the relative influence of each being determined by the geologic setting.

In the recrystallization that produces new minerals, temperature is the significant factor. Heat promotes recrystallization for the same reasons that it stimulates other kinds of chemical reaction. Recrystallization is also greatly assisted by fluids, since most recrystallization takes place through the dissolving of unstable substances and the precipitation of the new phase. Although some minerals are stable through a wide range of physical conditions, many individual minerals and particular mineral assemblages cannot persist above a fixed limiting temperature. When this is exceeded, the chemical constituents are regrouped in new combinations. Should the temperature continue to rise, these minerals in turn will be changed to another set. Porphyroblasts that interrupt a metamorphic structure can be interpreted as minerals that have developed late in the history of the rock. The reorganization always proceeds toward a state of equilibrium, a mutual equilibrium between the minerals themselves, as well as between the separate minerals and the environment.

The temperatures at which minerals combine is known for only a few mineral pairs and in still fewer has the effects of pressure been investigated. Consequently it is not yet possible to relate metamorphic reactions to a fixed temperature scale. Nevertheless the repeated and consistent association of certain minerals in rocks of known origin permits the use of relative and qualitative scale. Until the laboratory shall supply the necessary measurements it is appropriate to describe some metamorphic minerals as products of "low" temperature reactions (chlorite, talc), and others as formed at "moderate" temperature (phlogopite), and still others as "high" temperature minerals (olivine, pyroxenes). It would not be expected that any two minerals would be stable through the same temperature range. As examples, muscovite is found associated with both low and moderate temperature minerals, biotite and hornblende occur in rocks formed at moderate and high temperatures. Quartz is stable throughout the entire range of metamorphic conditions. Unless interfering factors are present, high temperature tends to expel volatile substances and so produces anhydrous minerals. Carbon dioxide is similarly removed, unless it is contained by pressures too great to permit its escape.

In theory, the transformations of sets of minerals to higher temperature associations can be represented as reversible equations. Actually the minerals formed at high temperature remain stable through indefinite intervals of time and down to any temperature experienced at the surface of the earth. Otherwise it would never be possible to examine rocks that had been reorganized under intense metamorphism. Apparently the reversed reactions do not take place with falling temperature unless special conditions are introduced.

The effects of pressure in metamorphism are largely mechanical and are seen in the resulting details of texture and structural arrangement rather than in the production of specific minerals. Strong directed pressure may crush a rock in various ways. In simple crushing a rock may be either brecciated or broken down to a finely granular mosaic of fragments (*cataclastic structure*). If the pressure results in a sufficiently strong differential movement, the rock in which it occurs is pulverized and "milled out" in the direction of movement. *Mylonite* is the name applied to the resulting material. The zones of thrust faults provide the most convincing evidence of the process, the effects of which are not confined to megascopic faults. Some slates owe their easy splitting to closely spaced planes that mark the direction of internal movement. Any crushing that takes place accelerates the metamorphic process as a whole, because by reducing the sizes of rock or mineral particles it exposes more surface area and thereby increases the rate of chemical change.

When a rock is not broken but responds to pressure by internal movements, the minerals with strong inequidimensional shapes may be rotated. Their longer dimensions come to rest in new positions, and thus the platy or bladelike crystals may be shifted until they lie approximately parallel. In this way a rock may acquire either a linear structure or one marked by parallel planes. The orientation of original minerals, as distinct from parallelism developed by recrystallization, is only possible in rock material that is partly fluid, or in rocks subject to plastic flow under pressure. The foliation in some slates is attributed, at least in part, to the rotation of micaceous or chloritic minerals. Carbonate rocks flow readily, but do not exhibit megascopic parallel structures because they lack minerals with the necessary shapes. The brittleness of most silicate rocks precludes the rotation of their minerals without fracturing, unless they are first "softened" by some other process.

The arrangement of lineation or plane structures brought about by crystal rotation is determined by the direction of movement within the rock. Usually the orientation of the long axes is parallel to the internal movement. The relationship between this direction and the direction of the pressure causing the metamorphism is complex and variable, involving questions that lie in the domain of structural studies rather than petrology.

Most slates and presumably all phyllites and schists owe their foliation to recrystallization that takes place under the influence of strong directed pressure. The foliation of these rocks, as previously described, results from the parallel orientation of flat and prismatic minerals. It is generally assumed that foliation develops by these minerals crystallizing with their long dimensions growing in the directions least constrained by pressure. This simplified explanation is probably correct, but it accounts only for the final stage. Tectonic forces build up gradually, and a long time interval separates the pre-metamorphic conditions from the environments where rocks undergo profound recrystallization. The intermediate steps may include many processes and their effects: the crushing of rocks, internal rock movement, rotation of minerals, rising temperature, and progressively tighter folding. Rocks may retain some signs of earlier stages, and the field relations often allow for considerable interpretation, but specimens seldom reveal direct evidence of the details of their metamorphic history.

In a general account of rocks it is appropriate only to indicate the complexity of the relationship between the attitude of foliation and the forces under which it develops. Under some circumstances minerals may crystallize with their long axes in the plane perpendicular to pressure. This would be the expected arrangement in a rock deformed by simple compression, but where it is possible to determine the direction of the forces involved, they are more frequently resolved as shear. In this type of stress the foliation plane is inclined to the directions of pressure. Lineation* in the plane of foliation is an equally complicated structure. Its analysis depends upon specific knowledge of the deformation history of the rock.

Reorganization of rock constituents under strong pressure promotes the crystallization of minerals with high densities. This would be expected under conditions that favor volume reduction—pressure is partially relieved by a closer spacing of ions. The effect is demonstrated by such heavy and typically metamorphic minerals as the garnets, andalusite, kyanite, and staurolite. Evidence based on mineral association indicates that some minerals crystallize only in the presence of directed pressure and hence are particularly characteristic of the foliate rocks. Staurolite and kyanite fall in this category. Conversely other minerals, including olivine, andalusite, and anorthite, appear to be unstable under shearing stress, but form in rocks metamorphosed under hydrostatic pressure. The compound Al_2SiO_5 appears in both groups but as minerals with different specific gravities, kyanite (3.6) and andalusite (3.2).

Types of Metamorphism

Metamorphism may result from the effects of a single agency or of several. It may be intense or comparatively mild. When two or more factors contribute to metamorphism, any one may exercise a greater influence than the others and dominate the resulting rock with its specific characteristics. Finally, rocks may pass through more than one cycle of metamorphic processes. For these reasons the different categories of metamorphism are linked by a series of gradations, and the rocks similarly exhibit intermediate stages from one type to

* For a clear and detailed account of lineation, the reader should consult *Lineation* by Ernst Cloos, Memoir 18 of the Geological Society of America. Each of the several standard books on structural geology discusses the attitude of foliation and related structures with relation to stress.

another. Nevertheless the metamorphic processes lend themselves readily to a natural grouping, a classification based both upon the controlling factors and the particular geologic setting where they operate. The distinctive types of metamorphism are listed and summarized as follows:

I THERMAL METAMORPHISM changes rocks through an increase of temperature, with little or no influence from added pressure. The effects are localized in the vicinity of igneous intrusions or extrusions, and the temperature varies through a wide range. Typical products are hornfels and some quartzites, marbles, and ophicalcites. The term **contact metamorphism** is sometimes used with the same meaning, but is more often employed to indicate the introduction of new material from the igneous source in addition to the effects produced by elevated temperatures. Both simple thermal metamorphism and contact metamorphism take place through recrystallization; textures and minerals may be changed, and although the original structure may be obscured or obliterated, no new structures are made.

II KINETIC METAMORPHISM is brought about by strong directed pressure without a notable increase in temperature. It is characteristic of zones of tight folding at relatively shallow depths. Kinetic metamorphism produces cataclastic structures and rocks with slaty fracture. Crushing and mineral rotation are more characteristic of the process than is recrystallization, but considerable recrystallization takes place in argillaceous rocks and limestone. Mylonite, granulated rocks, and some slates and marbles are typical rocks.

III DYNAMOTHERMAL METAMORPHISM includes the combined effects of strong directed pressure and high temperature, and occurs in zones of intense folding. In many regions it involves the country rock of tectonic belts extending for hundreds of miles along the strike. Of the metamorphic rocks exposed at the surface of the earth, by far the greater part has been formed by dynamothermal metamorphism. The rocks included are practically all the schists and phyllites, many slates and gneisses, together with most quartzites and marbles. Many intermediate processes are involved, but the essential change is the recrystallization that leads to pronounced parallel structures. It produces visible foliation or lineation in all rocks except those lacking the appropriately shaped minerals. With lower temperatures, dynamothermal metamorphism grades into kinetic metamorphism, with the change from directed to hydrostatic pressure and somewhat higher temperature, it becomes **plutonic metamorphism**. In places where erosion has exposed different levels of the lithosphere this gradation has been correlated with depth. Kinetic metamorphism is typically a near-surface process, plutonic metamorphism a deep-seated phenomenon. **Regional metamorphism** is a convenient term used to cover kinetic and plutonic as well as dynamothermal metamorphism.

IV PLUTONIC METAMORPHISM takes place at high temperature and requires intense pressure. The pressure is either hydrostatic or so nearly balanced that foliation and lineation are either obscure or absent. The inferred conditions so nearly resemble the environment associated with deep-seated igneous intrusions and are so far below our zone of observation, that it is difficult to postulate a clear line of distinction between igneous and metamorphic activity. The same uncertainty extends to many granitic rocks that acquired their characteristics in this zone. According to one hypothesis, granite magmas originate by the liquefaction of buried sediments as the ultimate stage of intense metamorphism at great depths. The rocks generally accepted as the products of plutonic metamorphism are the granulites, some gneisses, amphibolites, and eclogites, and feldspathic rocks with faint traces of gneissic structure.

V HYDROTHERMAL METAMORPHISM includes the changes brought about more or less exclusively through the action of hot water, acting either as a liquid or vapor. It may be regarded as a phase of metamorphism, or under the slightly changed label of *hydrothermal alteration* it may be classed as a destructive rather than integrating process (p. 141). It is often accompanied by the addition of new substances, or by the removal of others, or by both. Many rocks show the effects of hydrothermal attack, but the only rocks in which this is an essential and dominant process are serpentine and soapstone.

VI INJECTION METAMORPHISM. The invasion of foliate rocks by igneous emanations to produce the mixed rocks known as migmatites has already been described (p. 210 and Figure 26). Although injection may occasionally lead to the complete reworking of the minerals of the invaded rock, it is an auxiliary process rather than a separate type of metamorphism. For some rocks it is possible to demonstrate that the invasion took place after the host rock had undergone metamorphism; for others it seems probable that the injection and metamorphism were contemporaneous.

The several types of metamorphism are summarized in Table 22.

GENESIS OF THE COMMON METAMORPHIC ROCKS

Although no rocks are immune to metamorphic change, they differ vastly in their susceptibility to various kinds of chemical and mechanical stress. The response to metamorphism depends upon almost every characteristic that makes one rock different from another: resistance to crushing, the presence or absence of layered or foliate structures, grain size, porosity and solubility, the chemical inertia or potential activity of the minerals, and their stability with respect to elevated temperatures and pressures.

Sedimentary rocks, on the average, are far more vulnerable to metamorphism than the rocks formed in other ways. This is particularly true of argillaceous rocks and limestones. The constituents of these rocks are formed by surface processes and are stable within surface environments, and are easily modified under stress. In direct contrast, intrusive igneous rocks crystallize under the influence of high temperature and moderate to high pressure; large intrusions yield only when the agents of metamorphism approach maximum intensity.

Apart from their susceptibility to change, the preponderance of metasediments in the extensive metamorphic terranes is explained by the geologic pattern within which major tectonic movements operate. Periodically throughout the past, horizontal stresses have

TABLE 22.   Summary of Metamorphic Processes

Type	Dominant Factors	Geologic Provenance	Contributing Processes	Typical Minerals	Characteristic Rocks
THERMAL	High or moderate temperature, low pressure	Adjacent to igneous intrusions and extrusions	Recrystallization	Andalusite Grossularite Wollastonite Anorthite Olivine	Hornfels Quartzite Marble
CONTACT	As above, but with invading igneous emanations	Pronounced only in the vicinity of large intrusions	Recrystallization and replacement	As above, plus metallic oxides and sulfides	As above, plus garnet rocks and ore deposits
KINETIC*	Directed pressure, low temperature	Belts of folding crush zones thrust planes	Crushing Pulverizing Mineral rotation	Muscovite Chlorite	Breccia Granulated rocks Mylonite Some slate
DYNAMOTHERMAL*	Strong directed pressure, high temperature	Tectonic belts especially regions of geosynclinal sedimentation	Progressive recrystallization with rising temperature	Talc Chlorite Micas Amphiboles Kyanite Staurolite Garnet	Phyllite Schist Gneiss Quartzite Marble
PLUTONIC*	High temperature, strong hydrostatic pressure	Lower levels of tectonic belts	Recrystallization	Feldspars Pyroxenes Garnet Olivine Anhydrous minerals	Granulite Gneiss Amphibolite Eclogite
HYDROTHERMAL	Moderate temperature, water or water vapor	in igneous rocks with end stage water, wherever heated water circulates	Hydration Replacement	Talc Serpentine Clay minerals Epidote	Soapstone Serpentine
INJECTION	High temperature mobile igneous emanations	Regions invaded by batholithic intrusions	Recrystallization, replacement, substitutions following the igneous reaction series	Feldspars Pyroxenes Amphiboles Micas Garnet	Banded gneiss injected schist Migmatite Pseudo-granite

* Regional.

accumulated in the outer shell of the earth, building up slowly and involving regions many hundreds of miles long. When the lithosphere is no longer able to withstand these pressures, the rocks that fail and adsorb most of the movement are the ones previously laid down in subsiding depositional basins. Because of their layered structure, they yield largely by folding. Thus the geosynclines become the fold belts, and their rocks are deformed in varying degree, from simple open folds, through kinetic and dynamothermal to plutonic metamorphism.

Although the rocks within geosynclines are largely sediments, they may include lava flows and pyroclastics and occasionally sills, dikes, or other minor intrusions. In considering regional metamorphism, it is convenient to include these igneous rocks with the sediments in which they are intercalated; they are exposed to the same conditions, are similarly folded, and are made over to new rocks with broadly similar characteristics.

Metamorphism has only a limited effect upon the firm and massive units of the lithosphere; the batholithic intrusions and the crystalline metamorphic complexes. Pressure may lead to local crushing and milling in the zone of differential movement along thrust planes. Otherwise metamorphism is negligible. They remain as inert and stable blocks in the crust of the earth, unless a cycle of plutonic metamorphism or injection is brought on by liquefication at great depth or by the rise of new magmas.

Regional Metamorphism of the Layered Rocks

Regional metamorphism is loosely divided into *low-*, *medium-*, and *high-grade* metamorphism according to the intensity of metamorphic action. This is a purely qualitative grouping that combines the effects of all the metamorphic agencies. In the zone system of Grubenmann, rocks are classified according to the metamorphic environments that produce them. The rocks of the **epizone** are formed at shallow depths by relatively low temperatures but usually under directed pressure. The **mesozone** is a deeper level where both temperatures and pressures are higher than in the epizone, and the rocks are more completely changed. In the deepest zone, the **katazone,** the environment is one of high temperatures and strong hydrostatic pressure. These zones correspond roughly to the conditions that bring about kinetic, dynamothermal, and plutonic metamorphism respectively. The more precise* methods of classifying

* The most recent and exact system of metamorphic rock classification is Eskola's grouping according to facies. Each facies or subfacies embraces all the rocks characterized by a certain mineral assemblage. This system subordinates the original rock type and geologic setting to the equilibrium relationships of minerals under various

metamorphic rocks entail the recognition of minerals that cannot be identified by megascopic methods.

When argillaceous rocks undergo progressive metamorphism, their constituents are reorganized through a corresponding series of adjustments. Other rocks of complex chemistry are similarly affected, but are less sensitive than the argillaceous rocks to differences of pressure and temperature, and so exhibit fewer recognizable changes. In a series of rocks in close juxtaposition, the intensity of metamorphism can be approximated by using the condition of the argillaceous rocks as a standard.

Shale, folded and subsequently subjected to metamorphic influences that rise in intensity, will normally be changed first to slate, then to phyllite, and from this through a series of schists. If it proceeds beyond the schist stage, its history is problematic. Injection may convert it to a banded gneiss by lit-par-lit invasion, or plutonic metamorphism may change it to a streaked gneiss or granulite.

The change to slate requires only directed pressure strong enough to squeeze the rock into tightly closed folds. An internal movement that approaches plastic flow may orient the flat clay minerals, and the same movement may or may not impart a fracture cleavage. The stage at which recrystallization becomes appreciable depends both on the temperature and the chemistry of the rock. The foliation of roofing slate, as previously noted, results from the recrystallization of mica or chlorite in parallel planes.

Progressive growth of crystals, presumably under somewhat higher temperatures, changes the slate to a rock coarse enough to be described as phyllite. At this stage the foliation is usually crenulate. With further increase of temperature the crystals continue to grow larger, and other minerals develop. Although the change to schist is transitional, it may be arbitrarily fixed at the stage where individual crystals become visible, or when the muscovite is coarse

---

degrees of temperature and pressure and is based therefore on physical chemistry. The most recent account of facies is contained in *Evolution of the Metamorphic Rocks* by F. J. Turner, Memoir 30 of the Geological Society of America. A somewhat similar approach is used in the detailed mapping of metamorphic terranes. Minerals that do not appear until metamorphism has reached a certain intensity are used as guides to label and limit the zones in which they occur. For example, the map of an area of schist is divided by lines to separate the rocks in which biotite, garnet, or some other mineral, appears, from those where it is absent.

enough to give the rock its characteristic tinsel luster. Both muscovite and quartz are expected constituents in schists produced from argillaceous rocks. Various "new" minerals appear as a result of further recrystallization under rising temperature. Biotite and garnet can be taken to indicate an intermediate stage of dynamothermal metamorphism; staurolite and kyanite crystallize at higher temperature. Many exceptions are known to this order, and the development of any mineral depends upon the availability of its constituents. Both garnet and staurolite are strongly idioblastic, and garnet porphyroblasts often attain diameters of several centimeters and make up a large part of the rock.

Under the same conditions that change shale to slate or phyllite, limestone and dolomitic limestone become marble. The process involves only the recrystallization of calcite and dolomite to coarser textures. New minerals do not become conspicuous until rising temperature begins to dissociate some of the carbonates and expel carbon dioxide. Both lime and magnesia, but particularly the magnesia, are highly active substances, and they combine readily with whatever arenaceous or argillaceous materials may be present. In the presence of available silica, the high-temperature metamorphism of dolomitic limestone leads to the crystallization of tremolite, olivine, and diopside. Also some dolomitic marbles contain considerable phlogopite. All these minerals contain magnesium; its removal from dolomite may leave calcite as the only carbonate mineral. By the time an olivine-bearing marble has been exposed, the olivine has often been converted to serpentine, thereby changing the rock to a serpentine marble or ophicalcite. The dynamothermal metamorphism of nondolomitic limestone seldom gives rise to silicate minerals that can be recognized in hand specimens, however when these limestones undergo thermal or contact metamorphism, the lime set free from calcite can unite with silica to form wollastonite, or with clay minerals to make grossularite or anorthite.

Highly quartzose sandstones are much less susceptible to metamorphism of all kinds than the argillaceous rocks and limestones. Hence a sandstone retaining its sedimentary characteristics may be interbedded with slates and marbles. Directed pressure strong enough to cause movement within the sandstone layers may crush the sand grains and give the rock a granulated appearance, but quartzite is not formed until the temperature becomes high enough to recrystallize the quartz. A quartz sandstone is subject to no further changes beyond this stage, so that quartzite can be found associated with phyllites, schists, or gneisses. The metamorphic history of quartzose conglomerates is similar. Pebbles may be crushed, elongated, or recrystallized. Sometimes they retain enough of their original shape to be recognizable in strongly metamorphosed rock.

During the metamorphism of argillaceous sandstone, the clay fraction is usually recrystallized before the quartz, so that low-grade metamorphism gives rise to rocks intermediate between crushed sandstone and phyllite. Stronger metamorphism changes argillaceous sandstone to quartz schist, usually quartz-muscovite schist.

Salic tuffs and lava flows follow a pattern that resembles the metamorphism of both the argillaceous rocks and sandstones. Phenocrysts may exist as relicts, while the aphanitic material undergoes recrystallization. Schists produced from salic igneous rocks may differ so little from metasediments that their origin could be determined only by chemical analysis.

Femic igneous rocks, such as basalt, are changed to chlorite schist by low-grade dynamothermal metamorphism. Increasing temperature converts them to actinolite schist, to hornblende schist, with or without garnet, and under plutonic metamorphism they become amphibolite.

Retrogressive Metamorphism

Retrogressive metamorphism includes the changes that take place when a rock that was formed by relatively intense metamorphism is altered within an environment of lower grade metamorphism. It does not imply, as the name might suggest, a reversal of metamorphic reactions. The usual conditions or retrogressive metamorphism are strong directed pressure, comparatively low temperature, and the presence of enough water to bring about considerable hydration. Megascopically, the resulting rocks would appear to be slates or phyllites, and they would be very similar to rocks formed from any crystalline material that has been crushed or intimately sliced by faults. The correct identification of any of these rocks and their interpretation require a detailed knowledge of their structural relationships.

SUGGESTIONS FOR STUDY

1. Examine specimens that illustrate the textures and structures listed below, making careful comparisons of those features that are either related in origin or similar in appearance:
   a. Schistose and slaty foliation.
   b. Banding and streaking in gneiss.
   c. Lineation, alone and combined with foliation.
   d. Fracture cleavage.
   e. Idioblasts, porphyroblasts, and injected crystals.
   f. Elongated pebbles.
   g. Augen structure.
2. Arrange appropriate specimens of slate, phyllite, and schists in a logical sequence to illustrate the effects of progressive regional metamorphism upon argillaceous sediments. Compare this series with analogous sequences showing the progressive metamorphism of basalt, impure dolomite, and argillaceous sandstone.
3. Calculate the changes in weight and volume that take place when metamorphism converts quartz and calcite to wollastonite. The method of computation is shown in Appendix B. Similar examples are represented by the conversion of dolomite and quartz to diopside, and also the development of garnet (almandine) from a mixture of kaolin, quartz, and limonite.

APPENDIX A

Care of Specimens

Labels

In collecting rocks it is essential to make and preserve a record of the locality of each specimen, and to use a method that leaves nothing to memory. A common procedure is to number each rock on a strip of adhesive tape that is attached when the rock is collected and to describe the location against the same number in the field notes. Generally this description should be detailed enough to guide another observer to the same outcrop. In some circumstances the location may be marked directly by a symbol with the accompanying number on a map or fixed by a system of map coordinates. As soon as rocks are brought into the laboratory the temporary field labels should be replaced by permanent ones, which also should be placed directly on the specimens. One highly satisfactory method for this is to paint a small rectangle with white enamel on a flat surface near the edge of the specimen. The necessary information is then lettered on this background with drawing ink. This label should always include the location and number, and it is advisable to record the collector's name and the date. Other data, such as the rock type or formation name, will depend upon the purpose for which the specimen was taken. Loose samples collected in bags are best kept in jars or transparent vials, and these should be labeled in the same way, with the number and location on the side rather than on the lid.

231

Appendix A

Collecting

For most geologic work fresh material is selected, but if weathering or another type of alteration is significant, it may be necessary to collect a series of samples to illustrate progressive change. Similarly, it is often desirable to take specimens at spaced intervals on either side of an igneous contact, or vertically through a sequence of sedimentary rocks. Unconsolidated material should be scooped rather than picked from a carefully chosen spot to obtain a representative sample.

Ordinarily it is enough to record the strike and dip of bedding, foliation, or other structures in the field notes, and to indicate the upper surface on the field label of the specimen, but if the rocks are to be used in structural studies, it is necessary to mark them in the field to show their precise orientation. This can be done in several ways. A narrow strip of adhesive or some other marking can be placed on a bedding or foliation surface parallel to the strike, with a second strip at right angles on the same surface to indicate dip direction. The respective bearings and angles can be recorded on the label or in the notes. A rock that displays no visible linear or plane structure can be marked with a line or a stripe to indicate the horizontal plane, and a second to show the vertical plane in a north-south or some other convenient direction. Numbers marked on adhesive tape with an indelible pencil remain legible in spite of wear and rough handling.

Hand Specimens

Rocks that are to become part of a permanent collection for reference or exhibition should be trimmed as conventional hand specimens. In their generally accepted form, these are rectangular in outline, approximately four inches by three, and an inch or more thick, depending upon the rock (Frontispiece). Their preparation calls for practice, and the beginner should start with sedimentary rocks that break easily along the bedding or with metamorphic rocks that split along a foliation plane. The first step is to secure a flat slab or flake of the required thickness. To strike a suitably thin piece from a massive crystalline rock it may be necessary to use a heavy hammer (three pounds or more). The trimming is a flaking process, carried on by striking the edges of the specimen. Each blow is struck with the long axis of the hammer head nearly parallel to an end or side. Failure to avoid this precaution nearly always leads to a transverse fracture across the rock. To secure straight edges meeting at right angles at the four corners, the final trimming may be done by tapping the edges with the flat side of the hammer rather than with the face. When trimmed specimens are prepared it is necessary to collect additional material to use for analyses or other tests.

APPENDIX B

Density, Weight, and Volume

Density, weight, and volume are related by the formula shown below. For convenience it is stated in three different forms:

$$d = \frac{m}{v}$$

$$m = d \cdot v$$

$$v = \frac{m}{d}$$

where d is density, m weight or mass, and v volume. Engineers use pounds and cubic feet and compute densities as pounds per cubic foot (lb/ft^3). In scientific work dealing with solids, the corresponding units of weight and volume are the gram (g), cubic centimeter (cc), and density is stated as g/cc, or specific gravity. Since 1 cc of water weighs 1 g, the specific gravity of water is 1.0, and the specific gravity of any substance is numerically the same as the weight of 1 cc of that substance.[*]

In rock calculations it is often required to convert the amounts of the constituents to and from percentages by weight and volume, and from these to compute the theoretical specific gravity. Such calculations are greatly simplified by assuming that a sample has

[*] One cubic foot of water weighs 62.43 pounds. Since the specific gravity of water is 1.0, the specific gravity of a rock can be converted to lb/ft^3 by multiplying by 62.43.

Density, Weight, and Volume

a volume of 100 cc when the volume percentages are known, or a weight of 100 g when beginning with percentage by weight, as in the following examples.

1. A rock contains quartz 55%, dolomite 30%, and pyrite 15% by volume. Compute the composition by weight and find the theoretical specific gravity.

	(1) cc	(2) d	(3) g	(4) g	(5) g
Quartz	55	2.65	141	46.5	47
Dolomite	30	2.9	87	28.7	29
Pyrite	15	5.0	75	24.8	25
	100		303	100.0	101

The volume of each mineral (column 1) is multiplied by its specific gravity (2) to yield the weight (3) of each mineral in the original 100 cc of rock. The total weight of the minerals (303 g), divided by the 100 cc gives the rock a specific gravity of 3.03. The percentage by weight (4) is obtained by recalulating column 3 to a total of 100. The significance of column 5 is explained at the end of the following example.

2. Compute the specific gravity and the composition by volume of a rock with the following composition by weight: feldspar 50%, pyroxene 35%, olivine 12%, and ilmenite 3%.

	(1) g	(2) d	(3) cc	(4) cc	(5) cc
Feldspar	50	2.7	18.5	55.4	55
Pyroxene	35	3.3	10.6	31.7	32
Olivine	12	3.3	3.64	10.9	11
Ilmenite	3	4.7	.68	2.0	2
	100		33.42	100.	100

The volume of each mineral present in 100 g of rock is obtained by dividing the weights (1) by the specific gravities (2). The total volume, in this instance 33.42 cc, is then divided into 100 g to find the specific gravity, here approximately 3. The composition by volume (4) is computed by converting the figures of column 3 to a total of 100.

In these and all similar computations the results should be stated with the same number of significant figures that appear in the original data. If this is not done the final figures are misleading in that they suggest a degree of accuracy that cannot be achieved. For this

235

reason the three-place figures of column 4 in both the preceding examples have been reduced to two figures in column 5. This precaution is even more necessary when the original determinations are approximate.

It is to be emphasized also that the specific gravity of a rock, computed from its constituents, is a theoretical and not an actual value. Even when the percentages of the minerals have been accurately measured, a computed density takes no account of openings that may be present. Somewhat similarly, when the specific gravity of a rock is measured by the usual method of displacement, openings may exist that are not penetrated by the water or other liquid in which it is immersed, so that the measured value is the bulk density of the sample, and not the specific gravity of a pore-free mineral aggregate.

If a rock contains only two constituents, their amounts by both weight and volume can be determined from the specific gravity. This assumes that the amount of pore space is negligible and that the specific gravities of the constituents are known. The method is illustrated in the following example.

3. A specimen of an iron formation has a specific gravity of 3.2. The only minerals present are siderite (3.9) and quartz (2.65). Find the percentages of these minerals by weight and volume, and the weight per cent of iron.

   Assume that a sample has a volume of 100 cc, its weight $(v \cdot d)$ will then be 320 g.

   Let x represent the cubic centimeters of siderite, and y the cubic centimeters of quartz, then

   $$x + y = 100$$

   Since each cubic centimeter of siderite weighs 3.9 g, and each cubic centimeter of quartz 2.65 g, it follows that

   $$3.9x + 2.65y = 320$$

   Solving the simultaneous equation thus,

$$
\begin{array}{rl}
3.9x \ + 2.65y &= 320 \\
2.65x + 2.65y &= 265 \\
\hline
1.25x \qquad\quad\ &= 55 \\
x \qquad\quad\ &= 43
\end{array}
$$

it is found that the 100-cc sample of rock consists of 43 cc of siderite and 57 cc of quartz. These are converted to weight percentages by the method used in Example 1.

	cc	*d*	g	g
Siderite	43	3.9	168	52.5
Quartz	57	2.65	152	47.5
			320	100.

The per cent of iron in siderite is Fe/FeCO ($^{56}/_{116}$) or 48.2%. When this is multiplied by the weight per cent of siderite in the rock, 52.5%, the per cent of iron in the sample is 25, to the nearest whole number.

Essentially similar computations can be used to determine weight and volume changes that result from weathering, diagenesis and metamorphism. Examples follow.

4. Compute the change of weight and volume that attends the conversion of calcite to dolomite as indicated thus:

$$2CaCO_3 : MgCa(CO_3)_2$$

	(1) Mol. wt.	(2) g	(3) *d*	(4) cc	(5) cc
$2CaCO_3$	200	100	2.72	36.7	100
$MgCa(CO_3)_2$	184	92	2.87	32.0	87

In column 2 the molecular weights are adjusted to give calcite a value of 100 g, and the corresponding weight of dolomite, 92 g, indicates a weight reduction of 8%. Similarly, when the volumes are obtained by dividing by the specific gravities, the volume reduction (column 4 and 5) is 13%.

5. Calcite, kaolinite, and quartz combine to form grossularite according to the empirical equation:

$$3CaCO_3 + H_4Al_2Si_2O_9 + SiO_2 = Ca_3Al_2Si_3O_{12} + 3CO_2 + 2H_2O$$

Compute the changes in weight and volume assuming that the carbon dioxide and water are both expelled.

	(1) Mol. wt.	(2) g	(3) *d*	(4) cc	(5) cc
$3CaCO_3$	300		2.72	110	
$H_4Al_2Si_2O_9$	258		2.6	99.3	
SiO_2	60		2.65	22.6	
Totals	618	100		231.9	100
$Ca_3Al_2Si_3O_{12}$	450	72.5	3.5	185.5	80

Appendix B

The molecular weights of the minerals involved are given in column 1. The sum of the weights of the combining substances is reduced to 100 in column 2 with the corresponding weight of grossularite. The loss of weight is 27.5%. The corresponding volumes, obtained by dividing the weights by specific gravities are listed in column 4. Column 5 shows a volume reduction of 20%, after the total volume of combining minerals has been adjusted to 100.

APPENDIX C

Three-Component Diagrams

If a rock consists essentially of not more than three components, its composition can be plotted as a point on a graph with triangular coordinates (Figures 29 and 30). Each corner of the equilateral triangle represents one constituent, so that a point situated at the apex indicates a mineral, an element, a liquid, or a compound, consisting of that substance alone. Similarly every point lying on an edge represents a composition intermediate between the adjacent corners, and every point lying within the triangle contains all three constituents. The relative quantity of each substance is proportional to the lengths of the altitudes drawn from the point to the three sides of the triangle. It is a property of the equilateral triangle that the sum of the three perpendiculars drawn from any point within the triangle is equal to the altitude of the triangle. Therefore, if the altitude of the triangle is taken to equal 100 units, the lengths of the three perpendiculars drawn from a point to the sides will also equal 100 units, and the length of each perpendicular will measure the percentage of one component. Thus in Figure 29A the points a, b, and c indicate compositions only of these substances. Point d shows a composition sixty per cent a and forty per cent c. The composition corresponding to e is thirty per cent a, fifty per cent b, and twenty per cent c.

Changes that take place through the addition or removal of a constituent, or of any mixture of the constituents will cause the

239

point to move. If, in Figure 29B point *e* represents a liquid and a mineral of composition *b* starts to crystallize, the composition of the remaining liquid will change along a line directed away from the *b* corner of the triangle, and if all the *b* constituent is removed, the resulting liquid will have a composition shown by point *f*. Similarly

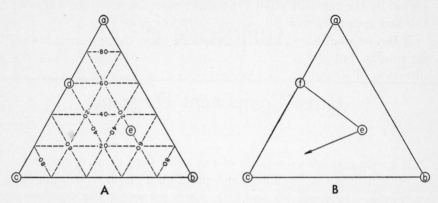

FIGURE 29.   Three-component diagram. See text for explanation.

the addition of component *c* will bring about a change of composition along a line trending toward *c*.

Triple Eutectics

In the following hypothetical example the triangular diagram (Figure 30A) is used to follow the crystallization of a triple eutectic. Points *m*, *n*, and *o* show the compositions of eutectic mixtures involving each of the three possible pairs. Point *t* represents the composition of the triple eutectic, the proportions in which all three constituents will crystallize together when the appropriate temperature is reached. The proportions of the constituents in the four eutectic mixtures shown on the diagram are:

$$m : a\ 50\% \qquad b\ 50\%$$
$$n : c\ 70\% \qquad b\ 30\%$$
$$o : a\ 65\% \qquad c\ 35\%$$
$$t : a\ 40\% \qquad b\ 25\% \qquad c\ 35\%$$

If the original liquid has a composition shown by *r*, the first crystals to form will consist of *b*. As these continue to crystallize, their removal changes the composition of the liquid along *rs*. When the liquid attains the composition of *s*, the eutectic mixture represented by *m* begins to crystallize, crystals of *a* and *b* crystallizing simultaneously, with the remaining liquid changing composition along the line *mt* toward *t*. When this point is reached, solidification is completed by the crystallization of all three components. This would be the first appearance of the mineral with composition *c*.

If the original liquid were represented by *x*, the sequence would be similar, but the removal of *b* would change the liquid in the direction of *y*, and the first binary eutectic to crystallize would be

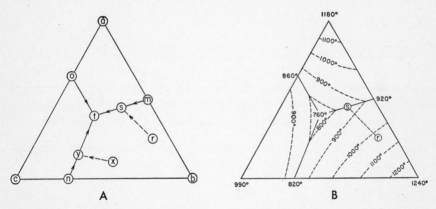

FIGURE 30.   Diagram of hypothetical ternary eutectic. See text for explanation.

n, and no crystals of *a* would form until the liquid reaches the composition of the triple eutectic at *t*.

Just as the binary eutectic point temperature is lower than the crystallization temperature of either of its components, so also is the triple eutectic point temperature lower than that of any of the three contributing binary eutectics. Temperatures are shown on triangular graphs by *isotherms*, lines of equal temperature closely analogous to the contour lines connecting points of equal elevation on topographic maps. In Figure 30B, continuing the previous hypothetical example, crystallization temperatures have been assigned to the three pure components and the four eutectic points, and the isotherms are drawn as broken lines. A liquid of composition *r* will cool until *b* begins to crystallize at a temperature of approximately 1060°. As

241

before, the liquid changes composition with continued cooling and crystallization until point *s* is reached, and here, at a temperature of about 840°, the crystallization of eutectic mixture *m* begins. Further cooling and crystallization finally brings the liquid to the composition and temperature indicated at *t*. Each of the three areas represented within the triangle can be visualized as a curved surface sloping generally toward *t*, each of the lines separating these surfaces simulates the bottom of a valley leading downward to *t*.

APPENDIX D

SUMMARY OF THE IGNEOUS ROCKS

Rocks related through possible gradations are connected by broken lines; quartz-bearing rocks are underlined. Occurrence and related textures are indicated by lettering, thus: DEEP-SEATED PHANERIC ROCKS; *hypabyssal rocks, intrusive porphyries;* effusive rocks, aphanites, glasses, pyroclastics.

GLASSES, PYROCLASTICS	APHANITIC EFFUSIVES	HYPABYSSAL ROCKS	COMMON PHANERIC ROCKS	ABERRANT TYPES, DIFFERENTIATES	FELDSPAR
obsidian	rhyolite	rhyolite porphyry	GRANITE	NEPHELINE SYENITE---phonolite	POTASH FELDSPAR
pitchstone		quartz porphyry	GRANODIORITE	SYENITE------trachyte	SODIC PLAGIOCLASE
pumice	dacite	dacite porphyry	QUARTZ DIORITE	GRANITE PEGMATITE	
vitrophyres	andesite	andesite porphyry	DIORITE		INTERMEDIATE PLAGIOCLASE
		?	?	ANORTHOSITE	
tachylyte	basalt	dolerite (diabase)	GABBRO	PYROXENITE	CALCIC PLAGIOCLASE
				PERIDOTITE	FELDSPAR-FREE FEMIC ROCKS
				SERPENTINE--- ? -	
				DUNITE	

243

APPENDIX E

SUMMARY OF THE SEDIMENTARY ROCKS

SEDENTARY ROCK	TRANSPORTED CLASTICS		TRANSITIONAL MIXED ROCKS	CHEMICAL DEPOSITS		
	TEXTURAL DIVISIONS	VARIETIES		ESSENTIAL COMPOSITION	CHEMICAL and TEXTURAL VARIETIES	
VARIOUS BRECCIAS	GRAVEL, COARSER RUDYTES CONGLOMERATE	till, tillite boulder clay arkosic conglomerate				
TALUS DEBRIS			CLASTIC LIMESTONES coquina shell limestone oolitic limestone	LIMESTONE	magnesian limestone dolomitic limestone lithographic limestone chalk travertine tufa crystalline limestone cherty limestone	
	SANDS, SANDSTONES	quartzose ss. feldspathic ss. arkose glauconitic ss. argillaceous ss. sedimentary quartzite graywacke	calcareous ss. arenaceous ls. argillaceous ls.			
RESIDUAL SOILS				SILICIOUS ROCKS	cherts diatomaceous earth	
	SILTS SILTSTONES	graywacke arenaceous shale loess	carbonaceous ss. carbonaceous shale	CARBONACEOUS DEPOSITS	peat lignite coal	
LATERITES						
bauxitic	CLAYS, SHALES	argillite ferruginous shale	calcareous shale ferruginous shale	EVAPORATION PRODUCTS	gypsum anhydrite salt	
ferruginous			ferruginous cherts	FERRUGINOUS ROCKS	bedded hematite siderite "iron formations"	

244

APPENDIX F

SUMMARY OF THE METAMORPHIC ROCKS

ORIGINAL COMPOSITION	THERMAL, HYDROTHERMAL METAMORPHISM	KINETIC-------DYNAMOTHERMAL METAMORPHISM------- Directed pressure ⟹ ⟶ increasing temperature ⟹		PLUTONIC and INJECTION METAMORPHISM
ALUMINOUS	HORNFELS	SLATE ----GRAPHITE SCHIST----	KYANITE SCHIST GRANULITE
		PHYLLITE MUSCOVITE SCHIST ----GNEISS----	BIOTITE SCHIST STAUROLITE SCHIST
FELDSPATHIC	EPIDOTE ROCKS	MYLONITE CHLORITE SCHIST	INJECTION GNEISS MIGMATITE
		-------- CONGLOMERATE GNEISS	
SILICIOUS	QUARTZITE	-------- QUARTZITE --------	
CALCAREOUS		-------- MARBLE --------	
DOLOMITIC		--------DOLOMITIC MARBLE--------	
		OPHICALCITE	TREMOLITE SCHIST ACTINOLITE SCHIST
FEMIC	SERPENTINE	CHLORITE SCHIST HORNBLENDE SCHIST	AMPHIBOLITE
	SOAPSTONE	TALC SCHIST	ECLOGITE

245

APPENDIX G

General Review Questions

1. Of the following lists of minerals, some represent typical rocks, and the others are associations unlikely to occur in nature. Name the rocks that are indicated by appropriate mixtures and explain why the other associations are improbable.
   a. Labradorite, quartz, biotite.
   b. Hornblende, andesine, quartz.
   c. Graphite, muscovite, quartz.
   d. Dolomite, olivine, diopside.
   e. Quartz, chalcedony, calcite.
   f. Potash feldspar, garnet, muscovite, tourmaline, quartz.
   g. Hornblende, quartz, garnet.
   h. Glauconite, quartz, calcite.
   i. Alkali feldspar, soda-pyroxene, nepheline.
   j. Chlorite, garnet, staurolite.
   k. Gypsum, anhydrite, "kaolin," glauconite.
   l. Andalusite, staurolite, kyanite, garnet.
2. List the rocks (igneous, sedimentary, metamorphic) that are essentially mixtures of feldspar, quartz, and mica. Why is this a common mineral association?
3. From what different causes may rocks be black?
4. A light-colored lava exhibits phenocrysts of potash feldspar as its only recognizable mineral. What categories might such a rock represent?

246

5. What conditions tend to produce particularly coarse textures in (a) igneous, (b) sedimentary, (c) metamorphic rocks?
6. What factors contribute to the high densities of the heavier rocks?
7. Some specimens of slate, hornfels, and shale tend to split evenly into thin, smooth parallel plates. What characteristics would serve to tell these rocks apart?
8. List the factors that determine the degree of roundness of a transported rock or mineral fragment.
9. Which rocks from the three major classes are especially difficult to break and trim? What various properties contribute to their durability?
10. Prepare a table to include the minerals, textures, and structures that afford reliable evidence for the (a) igneous, (b) sedimentary, (c) metamorphic origins of the specimens that display them.
11. Fine volcanic ash has settled to the floor of a lake. It consists of even layers and contains well-preserved fossils. Is this accumulation to be regarded as igneous or sedimentary?
12. List the rocks, regardless of origin, that contain the largest quantities of these constituents.
    a. Silica (more than 70%)   d. Alumina
    b. Magnesia   e. Lime
    c. Alkalies (soda and potash) f. Combined water
13. Why is pyrite widely distributed in rocks?
14. Why are argillaceous sediments commonly richer than coarse sandstones in carbonaceous material?
15. Granite and olivine gabbro weather to form residual soil under similar conditions of high temperature and abundant moisture. Compare the kinds and relative quantities of weathering products.
16. Outcrops of granite and coarse conglomerate occur close together, but the actual contact is nowhere exposed. What evidence, obtained solely from a collection of specimens, might suggest (a) a sedimentary or (b) an intrusive contact? (Disregard the possibility of a fault contact.)

Appendix G

17. What substances, other than argillaceous clays and shales, consist essentially of clay-size, clastic particles?
18. An hypothetical rock consists only of calcite and magnetite and contains no pore space. The specific gravity is 3.6. Calculate the amounts of these minerals by weight and volume, and find the percentage of iron.
19. Ferric hydroxide, $Fe(OH)_3$ (S.G. 3.7) crystallizes to form goethite. This mineral later changes to hematite, which, in turn, is converted to magnetite. Under what conditions might each of these changes be expected to take place? Plot the relationship between specific gravity and iron content as a graph and explain the resulting curve.
20. Calculate the depth of normal sea water that must evaporate to form a layer of halite (S.G. 2.2) ten meters thick.

Index

Index

Index

Index

Index

Index

Index

Till, 159
Tillite, 159
Trachyte, 63, 67
    average composition, 83
Trachytic structure, 67
Travertine, 176
Tremolite, 10, 15
        See also Amphibole
Triple eutectics, 240–241
Tufa, 177
Tuff, 62
Turner, F. J., 227

Undersaturated rocks, 76
Unsaturated minerals, 76

Variation diagrams, 81, 84
Varves, 173
Veins, 32, 33
    related to intrusions, 111
Vesicles, 32–33, 57–58, 61
Vesiculation, 62
Viscosity, lavas, 64, 66
    magma, 89–90
    related to glassy texture, 93
Vitrophyre, 57

Volcanic, ash, 60
    bombs, 60, 61
    breccia, 60, 124
Volume, 234
        See also Density; Specific gravity

Walker, F., 112
Weathering, 127
    bacteria, indirect effect of, 134
    chemical, 128
    controlling factors, 127
    organisms, influence of, 134
    oxidation and reduction, 133
    products, distribution of, 132
    products, tabulated, 131
    temperature, role of, 134
    volume changes, 135
    water, influence of, 128
Wet bulk density, 185
Wind deposits, 168–169

Xenoblastic crystals, 22, 197
Xenoliths, 54–56
    in lava, 68

Zoned structure, 101

256